No One Taught Me the Human Side of Islam

The Muslim Hippie's Story
of Living with Bipolar Disorder

~

Umm Zakiyyah

No One Taught Me the Human Side of Islam: The Muslim Hippie's Story of Living with Bipolar Disorder
By Umm Zakiyyah

Copyright © 2018 by Al-Walaa Publications.
All Rights Reserved.

ISBN: 978-1-942985-15-0
Library of Congress Control Number: 2018931584

Order information at uzauthor.com/bookstore

Verses from Qur'an adapted from Saheeh International, Darussalam, and Yusuf Ali translations.

Published by Al-Walaa Publications
Camp Springs, Maryland USA

Cover photo © by Shutterstock/ff-photo

Glossary of Arabic Terms

Allah: Arabic term for "God"

da'wah: educating others about Islam

deen: way of life, spiritual path, or religion

du'aa: prayerful supplication

fiqh: a scholarly explanation or understanding of an Islamic topic

haraam: prohibited or forbidden

hifdh (sometimes spelled *hifz*): memorization of the Qur'an

khutbah: religious sermon

kibr: sinful pride

niqaab: face veil

qawwaam: protector, provider, and maintainer of women in their practical, spiritual, and emotional life

riyaa: desiring admiration, praise and recognition from people instead of or in addition to God's pleasure

ruqyah: spiritual healing remedy

Salaah: formal obligatory prayer (performed five times each day)

shahaadah: spiritual testimony recited to mark one's formal entry into the Islamic faith: "I bear witness that nothing has the right to be worshipped except God alone, and I bear witness that Muhammad is His servant and messenger."

Shaytaan: Satan; the devil

Tawheed: Oneness of God; Islamic monotheism

ummah: universal community of Muslims

wudhoo': ritual ablution performed before *Salaah*

zakaah: obligatory charity paid to the poor

Bipolar Disorder in Psychiatry and Islam

According to the National Institute of Mental Health (NIMH), bipolar disorder (also known as manic-depressive illness) is a brain disorder that causes unusual shifts in mood, energy, activity levels, and the ability to carry out day-to-day tasks. NIMH further explains that people with bipolar disorder experience periods of unusually intense emotion, changes in sleep patterns and activity levels, and unusual behaviors. These distinct periods are called "mood episodes." Mood episodes are drastically different from the moods and behaviors that are typical for the person. Extreme changes in energy, activity, and sleep go along with mood episodes.

A person living with bipolar who is experiencing a manic episode will exhibit one or more of the following symptoms:

- Feeling very "up," "high," or elated
- Having excessive of energy
- Increased activity levels and being more active than usual
- Feeling "jumpy" or "wired"
- Needing very little to no sleep for long periods of time while remaining active during this time (i.e. different from insomnia)
- Fast talking about a lot of different things (often without making sense)
- Agitation and irritability
- Racing thoughts
- Thinking they can do a lot of things at once
- Engaging in risky behavior, such as reckless sex, spending lots of money, and impetuous decision-making (which are regretted once the episode passes)
- Inability or extremely reduced ability to control any of the above behavior during the episode

A person living with bipolar who is experiencing a depressive episode will exhibit one or more of the following symptoms:

- Feeling extremely sad, down, empty, or hopeless
- Having very little to no energy
- Inability to complete daily tasks
- Extremely reduced self-care and hygiene

- Extremely decreased activity levels
- Sleeping too much or too little while feeling unmotivated to engage in normal activities
- Inability to enjoy anything, even what is normally enjoyable
- Excessive worry and stress
- Difficulty concentrating
- Excessive forgetfulness
- Eating too much or too little
- Feeling extremely tired or "slowed down"
- Thinking excessively about death
- Suicidality, suicidal thoughts, or suicide attempts
- Inability or extremely reduced ability to control any of the above behavior during the episode

Additionally, people with bipolar disorder may experience psychosis, substance abuse, and symptoms of ADHD (attention deficit hyperactivity disorder). According to the NIMH the term *psychosis* describes conditions that affect the mind, where there has been some loss of contact with reality. During a psychotic episode, a person's thoughts and perceptions are disturbed and the individual may have difficulty understanding what is real and what is not. Symptoms of psychosis include delusions (false beliefs) and hallucinations (seeing or hearing things that others do not see or hear). Other symptoms include incoherent or nonsensical speech, and behavior that is inappropriate for the situation.

Bipolar Disorder in Islamic Jurisprudence

In Islam mental illness is a diagnosable condition that is traced back to the teachings of Prophet Muhammad (peace be upon him). Mental health is a condition of all Islamic contracts and is frequently referenced in all branches of *fiqh*. While some mental incapacitation results from the work of jinn, Islam recognizes that some mental conditions result from the chemistry and physiology of the brain. For this reason, experienced Muslim psychiatrists and scholars distinguish between mental conditions requiring *ruqyah* and those requiring medical treatment.

In *Forensic Psychiatry in Islamic Jurisprudence*, author Kutaiba S. Chaleby, who is a board certified forensic psychiatrist and member of the American Academy of Psychiatry and Law, explains the Islamic perspective of people experiencing mental illness due to the abnormal chemistry and physiology of their brains:

5

"Islamic law...recognizes a particular mental condition called *safa-hah*, which literally means extreme folly. It is not insanity, nor the consistent want of foresight that would indicate lower intelligence. A *safih* person behaves in an irresponsible manner, for example squandering his money, and in certain conditions, may lose his civil rights...According to some schools of Islamic law, the *safih* may also forfeit other kinds of civil rights such as holding certain kinds of job or profession" (2001, p. 21).

Chaleby further explains the Islamic perspective on insanity, a condition that is often manifested in a psychotic episode for people with bipolar disorder:

"Islamic jurisprudence classifies insanity into three types: absolute (or continuous), intermittent, and partial...

In this condition [of absolute or continuous insanity], the individual is judged to be completely and continuously unable to use his reason properly...

[Intermittent insanity is] the state in which a person can sometimes communicate at a reasonable level of conception, perception and cognition, but at other times suffers complete loss of his mental faculties, moving between full or partial remission and normal function. Such a person will be considered insane and not culpable during the active state of his mental disorder. He will be fully responsible for all his actions when he is not in that state. When in partial remission, he will be culpable for things that he is able to conceive and appreciate.

[In partial insanity], the person will have the ability to appreciate the nature of some of his actions, and understand certain circumstances. However, in other areas of life and different circumstances, he lacks the same appreciation. He is able to conceive and recognize certain matters and is aware of the reality of his environment, but is unable to perform the same functions in relation to other matters. Periods of exacerbation and a state of absolute insanity can occur at certain times. The partially insane person is legally responsible for those actions he is able to conceive and perceive as they are in reality. At the same time, he is not culpable for other areas of his life which he is unable to appreciate." (p. 22).

Though Islamic jurisprudence may or may not refer to bipolar disorder using the same terminology that is used in American psychiatry, both American psychiatry and Islam agree on the existence of the condition, which is defined by its presenting symptoms. Furthermore, Islam recognizes that these symptoms often manifest as a result of an abnormal physiological chemical reality in the brain. Thus, neither this brain abnormality nor its presenting symptoms is necessarily related to one's character, religious commitment, or contact with jinn.

Foreword

There are many issues involved in writing a book in the voice of someone else, and these issues are compounded when the experiences are being shared through the lens of mental illness. How do you know what is real and what is not? How do you authenticate each anecdote to ensure the greatest objectivity? How do you balance truthfulness with protecting the reputation and identity of others mentioned in the accounts? These are questions often asked by both writers and readers of true stories, and they are certainly valid concerns.

In responding to inquiries of this nature, particularly in the case of a story told from the perspective of someone with mental illness, I think it is important to note that mental illness is not synonymous with complete insanity. Yes, insanity is definitely a type of mental illness. However, the image of a "crazy person" living each day with absolutely no connection to reality or without any valid recollection of events is largely stereotypical. Just as there are different types of mental illness, there are different levels of mental illness.

In a 2014 report, the Substance Abuse and Mental Health Services Administration (SAMHSA) estimated that "42.5 million American adults (or 18.2 percent of the total adult population in the United States) suffer from some mental illness" (Bekiempis, 2014). These illnesses include enduring conditions such as depression, bipolar disorder, and schizophrenia. Practically speaking, what this means is that approximately one out of every five Americans suffers from some form of mental illness, and for the vast majority of these Americans, these mental illnesses do not prevent them from fulfilling daily tasks such as socializing, going to school, or working a job. In other words, these are functioning human beings whose life experiences are no less authentic than our own.

Interestingly, one of the greatest barriers that exist in removing the stigma of mental illness in our society is our inability—or refusal—to view those diagnosed with mental illness as full human beings. Their sadness and frustration, as well as their happiness and accomplishments, are no less or more valid than our own. Yes, there are definitely extenuating circumstances that must be kept in mind when addressing the specifics of particular life events of those living with mental illness. However, it is unfair to view their personal stories as inherently suspect, as if the processing of their own feelings, needs, and emotions are any less real because of their condition. In truth, *all* personal recollections of life events are inherently subjective, as they are confined to the limited and biased perception of the one recounting them.

Ironically, for those who view themselves as mentally healthy, one of the side effects of this self-ascribed view is the blindness to (or denial of) one's own delusions. Tragically, the "mentally healthy" often mistake their emotional convictions for truthfulness and objectivity when they are often rooted in destructive human pride. In this vein, those living with mental illness arguably have more self-awareness and honesty than others, thereby making their recollections of events that much more trustworthy. At least those living with mental illness often know their limitations and thus do not assume themselves to possess complete objectivity and infallibility.

I reflect on the troubling phenomenon of self-proclaimed "objectivity" in my personal journal:

> *Of the most arrogant and self-deluding claims is one of complete objectivity. Only God holds the ability to see reality in its purest, truest sense, free of subjective human experience, emotion or bias. Excepting receiving direct revelation from the heavens in prophethood, no human can claim to speak and behave with flawless precision and correct action and perspectives. In fact, no prophet even claimed this.*

Nevertheless, there is a positive side to humans' inherent lack of objectivity. I reflect on this positivity in my personal journal:

> *In truth, it is our subjective human experience that forms everything we do—on a personal, family, community and religious level—and this is what makes us beautiful and valuable in the world. We each hold a necessary human perspective that forms each part of the single* ummah *body and human family. And those amongst us who realize the inherent subjectivity in their most coveted convictions and perspectives come closest to understanding the limited objectivity a human can experience on earth.*

Therefore, it is important that we do not confuse lack of objectivity with lack of validity. Subjectivity forms the very essence of human experience. Without our emotions and frustrations or our uncertainties and doubts, there is neither power nor authenticity to our "true stories." In fact, it is this inherent subjectivity that makes memoirs and anecdotes so much more enjoyable and relatable than rote "history" and scientific "facts." In other words, our human subjectivity gives our life stories a soul.

Even so, we must accept that subjectivity is inherently limiting and problematic where "factual accounts" are concerned. This problem is increased when these accounts include interactions with others, whose recollection of the "facts" may be significantly different from the one sharing the story. For this reason, wherever the identities of others are mentioned in this book, all names have been changed, and any personally identifying information has either been omitted or presented in as nonspecific a manner as possible.

Additionally, the focus of the book is on the personal struggles of Karen (who is known as Sakinah or "The Muslim Hippie" in her mental health advocacy work), particularly as it relates to being an American Muslim living with bipolar disorder in a newfound religious community. Thus, the details of others' lives are largely irrelevant. The purpose of Karen sharing her story is not to cast blame but to inspire sensitivity and understanding for others living with mental illness, especially in religious communities.

As Karen herself has acknowledged on more than one occasion—and as she repeatedly emphasized to me as she recounted some of the more deeply hurtful events: No one in her religious community set out to purposefully hurt her or to make her life unbearable. Like so many communities in America, whether secular or religious, the Muslims in Karen's community were genuinely ignorant more than they were heartless or malicious. Nevertheless, it is unfortunate that more often than not, both ignorance and maliciousness produce the same harmful result.

For this reason, Karen hopes that by sharing her story, the harms of ignorance will be lessened, especially in environments purporting to provide spiritual sanctuary to believers during their brief sojourn on earth. In this noble purpose, I pray that I have done her story justice while speaking in her voice and sharing glimpses of the heart and life of my dear friend and sister in faith.

Umm Zakiyyah
May 2017

Note to Readers

◆

The story I'm about to tell has a lot of dark moments and a lot of pain. It's very raw and frank. It's my truth, my story of life with mental illness. It's not meant as a criticism or critique of what went wrong in my life. I share my story to illustrate how stigma, lack of information, and fear can shape thinking surrounding mental illness and mental health issues. And I share it in the hopes that others who struggle like me are encouraged to seek help for their issues and begin to live a full life in spite of their challenges.

Maybe if I had known someone like me when I had first gotten sick, I would have made better choices and learned how to manage my illness sooner. I pray that my message helps others live well with the test of mental illness.

Ameen.

Sakinah "The Muslim Hippie"

June 2017

For those struggling to figure it all out on their own. I hope this helps, even if only a little bit.

"I have had many concerns about writing a book that so explicitly describes my own attacks of mania, depression, and psychosis, as well as my problems acknowledging the need for ongoing medication...I have no idea what the long-term effects of discussing such issues so openly will be on my personal and professional life, but, whatever the consequences, they are bound to be better than continuing to be silent."

—Kay Redfield Jamison, *An Unquiet Mind: A Memoir of Moods and Madness*

The following is a glimpse into the life of "The Muslim Hippie"
as shared with Umm Zakiyyah

PART I

Becoming Muslim, Denying the Self

"I have felt at times that I didn't have the right to even exist. Almost everything I was taught about being a 'good Muslim' meant living in denial of myself."
—from the journal of Umm Zakiyyah

1

The Human Side of Islam

◆

What is the human side of Islam? To me, it is taking into account the whole human being. It is putting Islam in the context of human struggle while not discounting the soul. And it is presenting the *deen* as its true self.

It is empathy over sympathy, compassion over cruelty, and patience over frustration.

It is treating every soul as flawed and in desperate need of Allah's mercy. And it is never giving up.

It is not the expectation of perfection, but the embracing of one's humanity—that state where perpetual imperfection knows its Lord. And it is meeting every person where he or she is, not where we expect them to be.

It is not about always being right. It is about remaining on the right path, that spiritual road where you always have permission to get back up after you fall. Over and over again.

It is encouraging, not shaming.

It is understanding, not blaming.

It is reminding, not condemning.

But more than anything, it is the life path treaded by the broken, the weak, and the needy—those souls who are ever mindful that the dirt from which they were created is part of them still. And it is knowing that spiritual purification is a continuous action, not a static state.

But no one taught me this. I had to learn it on my own. I would be lying if I said that there aren't parts of me that are still angry. It is frustrating to look back and realize that the Muslim community I was part of after converting to Islam put so much pressure on me to deny my humanity and fit into their narrow version of the faith. I cannot fathom why they were so repulsed by the small glimpse of Karen the human being, when she was the same human being in whom Allah saw so much good that He guided her to Islam.

I cannot understand why they punished me so severely for not living up to the standards of the saintly "Sakinah" they'd constructed in their minds. Why did they hate me so much for not playing the lead role in the religious fantasy they created of me? Why did they resent me for not living up to that fantasy I played no voluntary part in creating? And why was I accused of betraying *them* when they stabbed *me* in the back when I needed them most?

Why am I still Muslim? Why do I even bother? These are questions that have haunted me in my weakest moments. The unrelenting cruelty, the constant backbiting, and the public spreading of my faults—by my very own Muslim brothers and sisters in faith—have created deep emotional wounds that I don't even know how to reach, let alone heal. And to think that their mistreatment of me was at its worst when I needed their patience and compassion the most—during a bipolar episode— enflames within me a rage that I can only ask Allah's help in quelling.

But in my heart, I know I remain Muslim because Allah is my Lord, not the people. Even as I have to protect my Islam—and my mental health—by staying away from most Muslims. Particularly the ones I was tested with being around after I became Muslim.

Besides, I didn't choose Islam. Allah decided that He wanted me to be Muslim. I wasn't looking for Islam. So no one's going to kick me out except Allah. When Allah is done with me, He will be done. And that's the end of it.

But I hope He's never done with me, even when I feel like giving up on myself.

2

Finding Direction

When I was in college, I didn't have a direction. I was struggling.

I remember sitting on my bed in my University of Maryland dormitory room and saying to myself, *God must be preparing me for something special.* And these words I got from a close friend who was Catholic, who had said to me some time earlier, "You know, when you're struggling in life, God is preparing you for something special."

Throughout high school and college, I would often seek comfort in the company of friends and partying. There, amidst laughter and bonding with fellow academics, alcohol became a constant companion for me. Having a few drinks (or more) allowed me to escape my problems and drift into a space of no worries, even if it didn't offer complete peace. But being in the company of others made it that much easier to escape the isolating solitude of my own company.

But that year, in 1996, I was in my third year of college, and I had lost all my friends. On top of that, I was facing so many trials that I didn't understand. I was feeling so confused and alone and had no idea why all these problems were happening to me. At the time, I didn't know that I was bipolar and living through the depressive side of the illness. So on top of everything else I was going through, I was spiraling deep into the dark feelings of emotional confusion and social abandonment. I was even fighting thoughts of suicide.

It was my younger sister who suggested I join a local gym. I was an accomplished swimmer who had worked on and off as a lifeguard, so being physically active wasn't a completely novel idea for me. However, my sister felt that now was a good time to have a regular workout schedule through the formality of a gym membership. I liked the idea and agreed to join a small gym in Silver Spring, Maryland, where she herself was a member. I had no idea that this seemingly simple decision would change the course of my spiritual life forever.

While at the gym, I met an African-American fitness trainer who utilized the gym for his off-duty workouts, and we cliqued immediately. During the course of our conversations, I noticed that there was something distinctly different about him that I couldn't quite put my finger on. He was different from any other man I'd met, and I wanted to know what it was.

"I'm Muslim," Karim told me one day when I'd asked about it. At the time, I didn't know much about Muslims or Islam. But I knew that this was indeed what made him so different from others.

We eventually started dating, and during our time together, Karim spent a lot of time talking about Islam. I didn't want to hear about his religion, but he wouldn't leave the topic alone no matter how much it annoyed me. It was obvious that he was trying to convert me, and I made it clear that I wasn't interested. But Karim didn't seem to care. It got to the point where I felt suffocated by his complete disregard for my feelings during the discussions. Why wouldn't he just let it go? I didn't want to be Muslim, and I certainly didn't appreciate him pushing his religion down my throat.

Even when I was a child, I didn't like being told what to do. I was a real spitfire. If someone came at me saying what I *had to* do, I'd respond indignantly saying what I *wouldn't* do. I didn't like adhering to other people's *do*'s and *don't*s, and I certainly wasn't about to accept it from the man I was dating.

Karim's tactics became so overbearing that I was convinced that he was crossing lines that his religion didn't condone. I was determined to call him on it, so I got a copy of the Qur'an. When I opened up the Muslim holy book for the first time, it was with the intention of proving that he shouldn't be talking so harshly to me. I was determined to find any quote that I could use against him the next time we talked. I was sure I could find at least one passage that would say his approach was wrong.

But as I read the Qur'an, my furor was slowly abated, and I found my heart deeply moved by the words. A calm settled over me, and I forgot the reason I'd opened the Qur'an in the first place. I kept reading and reading, and I found myself profoundly connected to the Book. From that moment on, I knew I had to learn more about Islam. But I was determined to do it on my own.

However, I did tell Karim about my interest in learning more about Islam because I wanted to know where I could learn more independently. He took me to a masjid in Washington, D.C., where I saw *Salaah*, the formal Muslim prayer, being performed for the first time. I was deeply moved and felt a connection to the Muslims there. It was through memorizing and practicing those prayer movements that I began teaching myself how to pray.

Shortly thereafter, I found a local masjid near the university and visited it whenever I could. However, I wouldn't interact with anyone while I was there. I would look at the posters and information pamphlets posted in the halls, and whenever someone would walk up to me and ask if I needed help, I'd rush away saying "No thank you."

When I was alone, I read everything I could about praying properly, and I tried to imitate what I had seen at the D.C. masjid. But I didn't tell Karim that I was trying to learn the *Salaah*. I didn't want anyone's help. I needed this to be about me and me alone. I feared that interacting with Muslims during this early stage of learning would derail me somehow. I don't know if that was a correct assumption, but I was convinced of it nonetheless. I wanted this to be about only me and my Lord.

Despite my practice of the Muslim prayer and my continuous study of the Islamic faith, I didn't officially accept Islam, at least not yet. I continued my studies of the religion until the end of summer. It was during this time, on the day that my roommate and I shared a birthday, that I received the call that my grandfather had died. "This is a sign," my roommate told me as we reflected on the sad news. "You need to become Muslim."

Cheryl herself was Catholic, but she believed that God decreeing that my grandfather would pass away on the exact date of our shared birthday was His way of telling me I shouldn't delay my *shahaadah* any longer. I needed to convert to Islam right away. Personally, I knew deep inside that if I were to pass away without having accepted Islam, I would have no excuse in front of God. I had been asking God for guidance and deliverance from my problems, and I knew it was no coincidence that He had brought me to this point, where Islam was in front of me. The necessity of becoming Muslim weighed on my heart until I went to a masjid in Virginia that Friday and pronounced the *shahaadah*, the testimony of faith announcing my official entry into the religion of Islam.

I never saw Karim after that, but this did not disturb me. By then I knew that my meeting the Muslim fitness trainer was God's way of guiding me to Islam. Now that I was Muslim, the chapter in my life that included Karim was complete.

Days after becoming Muslim, I attended the wedding of a close family friend. Though I had been praying *Salaah* regularly in the privacy of my dorm room, no one other than my roommate knew that I had accepted Islam. I hadn't yet begun to wear hijab, so to my family and friends, I was the same Karen they had always known.

While at the wedding, some of the guests were whispering negatively about one of my cousins who wasn't present. "Did you hear about Shonda?" they were saying, disapproval in their tone. "She's Muslim now."

From the hushed conversations about Shonda, I knew that the news of my own conversion to Islam wouldn't be taken positively. But I was undeterred. I knew that becoming Muslim was the right choice for me. Days later, I told my family that I had accepted Islam.

3

Family and Religion

I was raised in a Christian home. Before my father met my mother, he spent time in a monastery. Nearly everyone in my family was connected to religion in some way. My mother was Southern Methodist, my father was Catholic, and my mother's father was a Methodist minister.

Growing up, I would listen to my grandfather's fiery sermons and marvel at how spirituality seemed to exude from him. I wanted to have passion for God like that. But beyond believing that He existed, I didn't feel connected to God in any significant way. I had a relatively religious upbringing, so I knew that we were supposed to pray to God for whatever we wanted or needed. However, the spiritual connection that I imagined my grandfather had with God, I didn't feel it within myself.

My mother got her spirituality from her father, and they were both pretty dedicated Christians. But I never believed in the Trinity. Fortunately, my parents didn't push their understanding of religion on me. What they believed about Jesus being God, the son, and the Holy Spirit just never made any sense to me. I'd always thought of God and Jesus as separate, and I couldn't understand how Jesus could be God's "son." So I just didn't believe it. But I don't think I was fully cognizant of my lack of belief in these concepts until I was in the church's Confirmation class, which was supposed to prepare me and the other Christian youth to formally dedicate our lives to Christ.

From childhood, I understood the concepts of right, wrong, and human sin, but in a simplistic way. You were supposed to do what was right and stay away from wrong. What I understood from this was that humans should try their best to stay away from anything that would displease God. But if you slipped up, being "saved" by Jesus acted somewhat like a buffer between you and God's displeasure. As a child, I understood the need to please God, but I didn't fully understand how Jesus could save me.

When I was in high school, I identified as a Methodist Christian because that's how my family described themselves. We went to a United Methodist church even though my father was Catholic. Because he went to church with us, I never learned much about Catholicism.

Though I wouldn't formally learn about Islam until college, my first introduction to Islam was through two classmates when I was sixteen. They went to a masjid in Silver Spring, and whenever they prayed, I remember being unable to understand anything they were saying. In retrospect, I feel like God was using them to introduce me to the idea of Islam before I formally studied the religion years later.

When I was in high school, I remember casually asking my Muslim friends about Islam and how it was different from Christianity and the Nation of Islam. They would answer my questions, but I didn't fully understand their explanations. I imagine that my lack of understanding had more to do with my lack of interest than their lack of clarity. I wasn't really interested in learning about their religion, but my questions gave us something to talk about. At the time, I considered myself Christian, and the idea of converting to another religion never occurred to me.

I do recall that one of my Muslim friends wanted me to become Muslim though. One day she told me about a young African-American woman at her masjid who had converted to Islam. My friend herself, like my other Muslim friend, was not indigenous American, so I suppose she imagined that connecting me with a fellow African-American would make me feel more inclined to convert. My friend suggested that I talk to the African-American convert about Islam, but I declined the offer and made sure to avoid the subject of religion from thereon. I didn't like the idea of anyone making suggestions about how I should live my life. Despite my own personal disconnect from Christian spirituality, in my mind, I was fine as a Christian.

But I wasn't fine. I wouldn't say my unrest was due to any spiritual turmoil though. I was drowning in sadness. Despite my generally lively, carefree exterior, the melancholy would hit me in waves. Sometimes I was so overcome with exhaustion that I would sleep for hours and hours, utterly incapable of doing much else. While my friends were out partying, socializing and enjoying themselves, I would be climbing into bed at seven o'clock in the evening and sleeping until it was time for school or church the next morning.

I suppose this dark feeling is what I'd imagined my grandfather's deep spirituality would save me from. But eventually the melancholic feeling would pass, and I would be back to the lively, bubbly Karen that my friends and family loved. When I was feeling happy, I was extremely energetic and personable, so I would go out with my friends and cousins and have a good time. But I did a lot of social drinking during these occasions, so much so that drinking became a habit for me.

At the time, I didn't think of my drinking as a problem because I wasn't hanging out with a "bad crowd." The parties and social events I attended were with fellow academics and accomplished athletes like myself, and I was generally with friends and families that my parents trusted and approved of. Though underage drinking was technically illegal, it was an accepted culture amongst American youth, though I can't say my parents would have approved if had they known.

My parents didn't tell me much about right and wrong during my youth, but I learned a lot by watching them. They talked to me about life and the things they'd learned, and these lessons stayed with me through adulthood. However, I sometimes wonder if I wouldn't have become such a habitual drinker had I been taught that drinking alcohol was wrong. I wonder the same about a lot of the questionable things that I was exposed to during that time.

Despite my personal struggles, I found tremendous enjoyment in sports. Both my sister and I loved sports, and our parents supported our athletic activities. I was on a swim team from age five to eighteen, and my mother was definitely a "swim mom." She was a referee and representative for the team for most of my swimming career. My father was also a referee at my meets. I often thought of us as a swim-team family.

Looking back, I would say I had a relatively normal American childhood and youth. For all appearances, my parents were a happy couple, and they made sure that my sister and I were happy too. We went to church every Sunday, and I sang in the choir. We visited all our grandparents regularly and went on family vacations whenever we could. When we took family vacations, it was usually at a resort near water. Deep Creek Lake, Ocean City, Rehobeth Beach. These are the memories of my vacations during childhood and youth, and I recall these trips as very relaxing and enjoyable.

4

What's Wrong With Me?

◆

The first time I saw a mental health professional was when I was in college. The waves of sadness would hit me in ways I had difficulty coping with now that I no longer lived at home. In high school, my family's busy schedule and socializing had distracted me somewhat from the depths of what I was feeling inside.

When I lived at home, there was always someone dropping by, someone we needed to visit, and somewhere we had to go. My aunts and their children were constantly at our house, and we were constantly at theirs. Even for family day trips, my aunts were usually there. I was around my cousins so much that they became like siblings to me. On Saturday nights, we would go out to dinner, and almost any day of the week, we would have sleepovers.

The laughter is what I remember most about that time. My family laughed together all the time. My dad was hilarious, and my mom had a great sense of humor too. We really loved to laugh. Even when I was sad, there was always laughter.

So what happened to me? Why did I get sick? When I think back on these fun times with family, it's really difficult to accept that I have a mental illness. I know now that my illness is genetic and that many in my family are living with a mental health issue. But bipolar disorder is difficult to wrap my mind around.

When I was in middle and high school, I was popular and had loads of friends, and I'm still in touch with many of them on social media. Sometimes when I'm chatting with them or scrolling through my feed, I wonder, *Why me? Why am I the one who got sick?*

But I'd quickly stop myself and remind myself that this is a test from God. There doesn't have to be a discernable reason for what is happening. It is what it is. In any case, God is in charge of everything, and knowing this helps get me through.

When I was in college and made an appointment with a mental health professional for the first time, I didn't know that I had bipolar disorder. All I knew was that my sadness was becoming increasingly unbearable and I was having difficulty managing it alone. I'd imagined that I might be depressed, but even that possibility didn't make sense to me. Everything in my life was going well. I came from a good family. I was an excellent student. So what was wrong with me?

I told the psychiatrist about my symptoms, and he diagnosed me with depression and prescribed Prozac for me. He also suggested that I join a gym and get on a vitamin regimen because he said it would help the medication be more effective. He also sent me to a therapist who he felt could better help me through my depression. I left his office having no idea that this was not something that I would eventually "get through."

5

Motherly Pride

◆

My mother was so proud of me. It was 1996 and a few months after I'd become Muslim, and I was on a panel sharing the story of how I'd converted to Islam. The event was hosted by the masjid near my university, and some Muslims I'd met during Islamic Awareness Week had recommended me to be one of the panelists.

My mother didn't initially like the idea of me being Muslim, so her pride in me wasn't due to my *shahaadah* story, but to the fact that her daughter was a speaker at the event. In retrospect, I'm not even sure she knew what the event would be about until she arrived. I'd told her that I was speaking on a panel and invited her to come, and naturally, she accepted the invitation.

I'd also invited a few friends, one of whom was a former boyfriend from high school. It was he who would, years later, tell me that my mother had pulled him aside at the event to say that she felt that my being Muslim was just a phase. "No," he'd disagreed. "I think this is a permanent life change for Karen." He was right.

I don't blame my mother for thinking that Islam was something I'd eventually grow out of. She was just speaking of what she knew of me. I'd gone through many phases in my life, and they all had passed. But through each of them, she was there by my side supporting me every step of the way. For her, it was the same after I'd become Muslim. Though she didn't believe my interest in Islam would last, she was supportive and loving toward me in my new faith.

But we did have our occasional arguments about religion, and they were always heated. Ironically, her strong disagreement with me had less to do with theology than practicality. She didn't understand why I'd chosen a life path so different from everyone else in the family. It just didn't make any sense to her. She herself was Southern Methodist because her father had been, and now that he had passed away, she felt an obligation to uphold his religion as a means of honoring his legacy. She felt I should do the same.

Ironically, the arguments she used to try to convince me to not remain Muslim only made my Islamic faith stronger. Nearly every point

27

she made was one that the Qur'an said that non-Muslims would use to justify not following the truth of Islam. One *ayah* in particular that I was repeatedly reminded of during our disagreements was this one: "When it is said to them, 'Follow what Allah has sent down,' they say, 'Nay! We shall follow what we found our fathers following.' Even though their fathers did not understand anything nor were they guided?" (*Al-Baqarah*, 2:170).

Fortunately, over the years, my mother's opposition to my religious choice tempered significantly. As time went on, it was apparent that she herself was realizing the spiritual veracity of my faith, though she was too attached to her father's legacy to ever say it aloud. However, she consistently accompanied me to masjid events and fundraising dinners. She even volunteered her services at the Muslim school from time to time. She frequented Islamic events so often that she had her own set of favored Muslim speakers. Her favorite was the community imam, whose deep spiritual knowledge and humble character she found inspirational.

My father was supportive of me in ways that even my mother couldn't be. He had spent time in the monastery as a monk, so many of the Islamic practices that my mother didn't understand, he never had questions about. So much of Muslim morality and dress mirrored his own experience as a Catholic ascetic. "I understand why you dress like that," he told me one day, empathy and compassion in his tone and countenance. He didn't say anything else on the topic, but I knew he wanted to let me know that as both a father and a Catholic, he loved and supported my spiritual practice. And that meant the world to me.

6

The Model Muslim

◆

The day I sat on that panel in 1996 with my parents and friends in the audience and shared how I converted to Islam was the beginning of the end for me. But I didn't know it at the time. Today, if anyone were to ask me about the trend of masjids and Islamic organizations putting new Muslims on public panels to share their *shahaadah* stories, I would advise against it. In my view, it causes more harm than good.

While the Islamic community benefits greatly from having converts share personal stories of how they came to Islam, there is very little benefit to the speakers themselves when they are new Muslims. There is no substance to these events, and there is no support. In fact, there really is nothing about them that addresses the individual needs of a person who has just made a tremendous life change and needs meaningful Muslim companionship and very specific spiritual guidance.

Though it is undoubtedly unintentional on the Islamic community's part, the role of the new Muslim at these "share your *shahaadah* story" events is more akin to that of a promotional model for a company or brand than anything inherently spiritual or beneficial to the new Muslim herself. The Islamic community wants to "market" Islam to a wider non-Muslim audience, so the new convert effectively becomes the celebrity face of the "Muslim brand."

I'm not suggesting that this marketing of Islam is a bad thing or that having a convert fulfill this role is wrong. This positive portrayal of Islam certainly has its place, especially given the anti-Islam climate of today. I'm only saying that this role is better fulfilled by someone who has been Muslim for many years than by someone who is just learning about their Lord and purpose in life. When a person is new to Islam and is asked to fulfill the very public role of being a Muslim representative at Islamic events, there are at least three major risks that cannot be overstated: He or she ceases to exist for any other purpose; he or she develops a false sense of self as a Muslim; and he or she is cultivating spiritually destructive diseases like *riyaa* and *kibr*—without having either the knowledge of their existence or harms, or the means to combat them.

Herein lies the formula for disaster. This is what I personally experienced, and I continue to suffer from the experience today.

Muslims who have had the opportunity to study Islam for many years would be well aware of the warnings in the Qur'an and prophetic narrations against assigning piety to oneself, desiring excessive praise, and exposing oneself to the harms of being publicly admired and idolized. But I was not. More seriously, I hadn't even learned about my spiritual heart in any significant way. Therefore, I had no idea there should be any cause for concern or that there existed any *du'aa* or Qur'an that I should be reciting to protect myself.

After all, it was knowledgeable, experienced Muslims asking me to sit on these panels, so I had absolutely no way of knowing that even the slightest caution should be observed in participating. Moreover, I had no idea that my participation in these public events, as well as accepting the various public roles thereafter, meant that the Muslims wouldn't believe I was a struggling human being like everyone else.

As a young American who had grown up admiring my grandfather's fiery sermons in church and positive role models like Oprah Winfrey on television, I viewed positive attention, public admiration, and the "rock star culture" as something praiseworthy, particularly when you were doing good things in the spotlight. Just as I had no idea about the warnings against *riyaa* and *kibr* or what excessive praise does to a person's heart, I had no idea what this very public role could do to the minds and hearts of the Muslims in the community. I had no idea all the things they would assume about me and what they would expect of me thereafter.

At the time, I was simply basking in all the attention. I was like a celebrity doing a multicity tour, and I loved it. Over the years, I was invited to speak on so many panels to share my *shahaadah* story or to talk about Islam that I lost count. Unfortunately, my role as an effective "Muslim rock star" built up my reputation as the "saintly Sakinah" who would ultimately fall from grace once my mental illness surfaced in ways I couldn't hide or control.

My first public speaking engagement on a Muslim panel was only a few months after I'd accepted Islam. During that time, I should have been fostering genuine Muslim companionship with women in the community. I should have been learning details about the spiritual purification of the heart and soul. I should have been learning the fundamentals of *Tawheed*. I should have been studying the Qur'an, not only how to read it but also how to understand it and live it. These basic lessons would have helped me get to know myself and my Lord during this delicate time. But these crucial opportunities were disrupted because I was too busy fulfilling the community role as "the model Muslim."

I don't mean to say that I knew nothing about the foundations of my faith or that I wasn't studying Islam when I wasn't on these panels. I'm a studious person by nature, so I attended classes whenever and wherever I could. I even taught myself Qur'an by listening to tapes and CDs. I had already taught myself how to pray. So when I speak of the disruption in my spiritual learning process while I was a new Muslim, I am speaking of a disruption that was less quantitative than qualitative. And when such a serious disruption happens at the beginning of the spiritual learning process, it is extremely hard to recover from. I'm still struggling to recover from it today.

Until now, by far, the most difficult part of the battle is my struggle to be seen as a fully worthy and valuable human being—and fellow Muslim—despite being a high-functioning woman with mental illness.

7

New Name, New Me

◆

I wouldn't have chosen a "Muslim name" had I known I didn't have to. But at the time, I thought an Arabic name was required as a spiritual rite of passage. Today I know that any name with a good meaning (or at least without a bad one) is appropriate as a Muslim name, irrespective of what language it is in. But there's nothing like public humiliation to convince you that something is wrong with you and the name your parents had given you.

I struggle with social anxiety. I always have. But as a youth, in between family events and school activities, I learned to mask it and do what was expected of me whenever I was around others. When I have anxiety, it might look to an outsider like I'm relaxed or even enjoying myself, but internally, I'm a nervous wreck. Generally, when I'm battling anxiety, I fare far better in structured situations than unstructured ones. Structure lets me know exactly what is expected of me, and it leaves very little room for uncertainty, error, or embarrassing faux pas.

Perhaps that's why I became relatively comfortable as a public speaker at masjid open houses and *da'wah* events sharing the story of how I'd accepted Islam. My *shahaadah* story was something that I couldn't get wrong. It was *my* story after all. So even if I did unwittingly make a blunder or two while sharing a few anecdotes from my life, no one would know, and no one would care. Yes, I'd still have terrible anxiety suffocating me if I later realized I'd said something wrong. But I could keep telling myself, "No one even noticed," until my overactive mind and paranoia settled down.

But unstructured events with very specific religious codes that I had no clue about? That's an entirely different story. But as the saying goes, *You do what you have to do.* And no matter how anxious and panicky I felt about showing up as a stranger in a public Muslim place while having no idea what would be expected of me, I had to learn as much as I could about my new faith. So I traveled forty minutes to Virginia to attend an Islamic class that I'd learned about from Karim before we lost touch.

I already knew enough about Islamic etiquette to cover my hair and wear long, loose clothes. Though I wasn't yet wearing hijab full time, I draped a cloth over my head before I drove to Virginia for the first time. When I arrived, I saw a sign for the women's section, so I entered there and found a seat on the carpeted floor. The Muslim women were laughing and talking amongst themselves as they waited for the class to start, but a few saw me and whispered salaams as I sat down.

Naturally, I didn't know anyone there, but I was pleased to see a White American woman speaking to the women about Islam. It was clear that she was the most knowledgeable of the group, and it gave me a bit of inspiration to see a fellow convert in such a respectable role. She was speaking so confidently and using Arabic phrases so seamlessly that I knew that I too could gain more Islamic knowledge. When she saw me, she stopped talking and studied me momentarily. After giving me salaams, she raised her voice and asked, "What's your name?"

All heads turned toward me, and my anxiety began to close in on me. But I found my voice. *After all, what's so hard about introducing yourself?* I thought. "Karen," I said, the confidence in my tone betraying the suffocating discomfort that I felt inside.

"*Karen?*" the woman repeated with a smirk. The disapproval in her tone was unmistakable in its condescension and mockery. "That doesn't sound very Islamic." Some women chuckled in agreement.

I was so mortified that I had no idea what to think, let alone say. The humiliation I felt was so indescribable right then, that till today I don't recall a single moment from that class except flashes from this crushing moment. There was my choking anxiety, there was the crowd scorning my name, and there was my mind frantically racing as I planned to go home and immediately find myself an appropriate name.

After the class, I didn't waste any time. I was determined to be a proper Muslim. It took me only a couple of days to find a book of Arabic names. At home, I quickly skimmed the alphabetized section for female names, and the name that resonated with me most was *Sakinah*. Typed next to it was the English translation *peaceful tranquility*.

Just reading the definition of *Sakinah* gave me calm. Yes, that's what I wanted to embody in my new identity: peaceful tranquility. So from then on, whenever anyone in the Muslim community asked my name, I told them "Sakinah." Just saying it gave me pride. I was officially Muslim now.

I had already recited the *shahaadah*, the official testimony of faith stating, "I bear witness that nothing has the right to be worshipped except God alone, and that Muhammad is His servant and messenger." Reciting this testimony had calmed my heart and offered my soul a peacefully tranquil spiritual path to pleasing God after I'd felt so disconnected from Him since childhood. And now, with a new name, calling myself "Sakinah" calmed my mind and offered me a peacefully tranquil social existence after I'd felt so disconnected from the Muslims at the class.

With my new name, I felt like a new person, and in many ways, I was. Choosing an "appropriate" name after that humiliating experience was like being finally chosen as part of an exclusive, coveted sorority. The mockery I'd been subjected to in Virginia was like the necessary hazing I needed to undergo before being accepted as part of the private club of Muslims.

Now that I was one of them, I would never be shamed for my name again.

But years later, I would be shamed for being myself.

Apparently, a mentally struggling woman drowning in the confusion of her own existence was not allowed in this exclusive club, at least not in the Maryland chapter I found myself part of.

When I think back to this time, I see myself proverbially flinging my arms wildly as I grapple for life. As the dark and confusing waters pulled me in, I would get occasional glimpses of my sorority sisters standing on safe ground. They were familiar faces that I associated with love, safety, and community. But now, they were shaking their heads at me while grimacing and whispering amongst themselves. And right before I went under and grew limp and lifeless in the deep waters of despair, I heard someone say, *Look at Sakinah, showing off and having fun in the water when she knows she belongs with us on shore.*

PART II
The Diagnosis

"Bipolar robs you of that which is you. It can take from you the very core of your being and replace it with something that is completely opposite of who and what you truly are. Because my bipolar went untreated for so long, I spent many years looking in the mirror and seeing a person I did not recognize or understand. Not only did bipolar rob me of my sanity, but it robbed me of my ability to see beyond the space it dictated me to look. I no longer could tell reality from fantasy, and I walked in a world no longer my own."
—Alyssa Reyans, *Letters from a Bipolar Mother*

8

Faith Is the Best Medicine?

I was on such a high after I became Muslim that I believed my newfound faith had solved all my problems. I had been deeply depressed and suicidal before reciting the *shahaadah*, and after I accepted Islam, I genuinely imagined that becoming Muslim had cured me.

I was in my third year of college when I made my last appointment with the therapist that I had been referred to after being diagnosed with depression and prescribed Prozac. I'd sat opposite the therapist in her office and said with full confidence and seriousness, "I'm Muslim now, so I don't need therapy anymore."

Till today, I remember the brief silence that followed and the hesitation in her speech. "So…" she'd said as if trying to find the most appropriate words in response. "You're Muslim?"

"Yes," I said, as if that explained everything.

Though I could tell she wanted to say I was making a huge mistake, she didn't discourage me from discontinuing therapy. But her expression said everything her words could not.

After I walked out of there that day, I stopped taking my medication and never returned to the therapist again. Though stopping therapy was not the best course of action for me, it was good that I stopped taking Prozac. While Prozac works well in managing clinical depression, it is contraindicated for those living with bipolar 1.

Of course, at the time, neither my therapist nor I knew that I had bipolar disorder, as many people with bipolar are often misdiagnosed with unipolar depression before finally receiving a complete diagnosis. However, the idea that I no longer needed therapy or medication for my condition because of my faith was a harmful misconception. Unfortunately, the assumption that faith replaces medical treatment and the need for therapy is common in many religious circles, amongst Muslims and non-Muslims.

Ironically, at the first *khutbah* I attended as a new Muslim, the imam discussed how Islam was not a replacement for medication or professional treatment of health ailments, whether mental or physical. However, as I listened to the Friday sermon, I didn't even relate the information to myself. Of course, I didn't know I had a mental illness. At the time, I was convinced that my previous depression was due to spiritual suffering. Thus, in my mind, converting to Islam had solved this problem.

I don't mean to suggest that before I became Muslim, none of my problems were inherently spiritual. There was definitely a significant part of my suffering that was rooted in the ailing of my soul. So naturally, this spiritual suffering only exacerbated my depressive episodes.

Since childhood, I had felt a gaping disconnect between God and myself, and undoubtedly, there is no greater source of sadness than feeling disconnected from the Creator. When I became Muslim and this spiritual void was filled, peace and tranquility reached the very depths of my heart. And without a doubt, this authentic spirituality healed the ailing of my soul. Till today, I draw on Islamic spirituality to bring calm to my heart.

However, my mistake was in viewing my entire earthly existence as spiritual and all my problems as rooted in lacking faith. Islam itself teaches that while authentic spirituality forms the foundation of one's life on earth, human life itself is multifaceted. I had erroneously assumed that there was only one significant facet to human life—spirituality—and that it was this singular concept that accounted for all happiness and sadness on earth.

I was not alone in this narrow assumption. In fact, many people of faith—whether Jewish, Christian or any other religion—view this assumption as a fundamental principle of spirituality. Some religious leaders teach that all sadness and depression are rooted in spiritual problems in the sufferer. While some sadness and depression do indeed have roots in spiritual struggles, it is grossly incorrect even from a religious perspective to suggest that all sadness, depression, anxiety, and mania are rooted in spiritual problems that can be miraculously fixed if the sufferer simply has "strong faith."

Faith is definitely an antidote in its own right, and it certainly is beneficial in addressing all types of ailments, even those that are non-spiritual. If I am unwell, I can pray to God to heal me, as God controls all things. Also, remaining positive and certain about receiving healing from God aids the healing itself.

However, praying for healing and remaining positive are not mutually exclusive to taking the practical steps necessary to treat the illness. In fact, it is God Himself who has provided the worldly means of treating any sickness. In Islamic tradition, there is a famous prophetic hadith that states, "There is no disease that Allah has sent down except that He also has sent down its treatment" (Bukhari).

Thus, even from an Islamic perspective, it makes no sense to believe that "faith is the best medicine" if we mean by this assertion that faith is the *only* medicine.

9

Marriage and Mania

◆

"I'm getting married!" I told my family just weeks after I met the brother. Believe it or not, that's exactly what I'd called him: "the brother." I didn't even know his last name. I was in my third year of college, and some Muslims in the local community had told me about a "good brother" who was looking to get married. Ahmad and I had met a few times in the presence of an imam (who was acting as both my marriage guardian and chaperone), and we liked each other well enough. Thus, marriage was the only logical next step—at least that's how simplistic it had been presented to me at the time. I was told that in Islam there is no dating or casual relationships with the opposite sex, so "getting to know each other better" was not really an option.

"You're getting *married*?" my mother said as if I'd completely confused her. "To *who*?"

Looking back, I cringe at how naïve I was at the time. As cliché as it sounds, there is so much I would do differently had I known then what I know now. But even with 20-20 hindsight, I don't believe I would have chosen a different life partner. Ahmad was indeed a blessing for me, and he remains so today. However, I was lucky. Other new Muslims who were taught such extreme restrictions on male-female interactions didn't fare so well in their marriage pursuits.

Today I realize that the overly simplistic way that I was taught about dealing with men was more cultural than Islamic. The Muslim community that I was part of at the time was comprised of mostly immigrants to America and their adult children or grandchildren. Although the community's marriage practices were not un-Islamic per se, they certainly did not represent the only authentic options available to practicing Muslims. Despite many of the congregants being first or second generation Americans themselves, they were largely disconnected from the American Muslim experience, particularly that of those who had converted to Islam. Thus, their marriage practices were rooted more in time-honored traditions from their home countries than in the practical reality of American life.

I do not mention these non-American cultural practices to discredit them. In fact, many of these practices do in fact represent the Islamic ideal in terms of how marriage should be pursued within the bounds of our faith. However, the problem lies in many immigrant communities' inability to distinguish the Islamic ideal from Islamic requirements. Islamic ideals work well for men and women with large Muslim families who are intermarrying with other large Muslim families whom they know well. However, these "Islamic ideals" are no longer ideals when they are applied to converts to Islam with absolutely no Muslim family.

The fact that my own parents and family were not included as important parts of my marriage pursuit is just one glaring example of what is wrong with "Islamic ideals" being presented as Islamic requirements. Practically speaking, my sentiments on this topic can be summarized in the following reflection by the character Renee in Umm Zakiyyah's novel *Realities of Submission*:

> Till today, I don't think those who come from large Muslim families can comprehend the tremendous difficulty it would be for a convert to Islam to not use even the telephone to talk to a potential mate. In the absence of a male relative representing us, not to mention the dearth of Muslim family themselves, marriage becomes an unimaginably delicate and complicated pursuit that cannot be held to stringencies that are, in many cases, more ideal than they are religious mandates.
>
> Yet, still, I cannot help but feel a tinge of jealousy for those with Muslim fathers, uncles, cousins, and siblings. How I wish I had the luxury of knowing someone who loved me would take care of finding a suitable mate on my behalf. As a teenager I would have scoffed at what I saw as an "arranged marriage," but today experience has taught me that it is most prudent to have someone who knows and cares for me sift through potential mates before bringing them before me. Then and only then should I select a lifelong mate.
>
> This method is so much more promising, not to mention successful long-term, in pursuing marriage than feeling your way in the dark— even with a well-intended imam by your side. Internet sites, I-heard-of-a-good-brother-my-friend-knows, green-card marriages, and sheer "luck" have truly taken their toll on those who have accepted Islam. The problems suffered by converts who have no Muslim relatives is so rampant that I now believe it is wisest, though not obligatory, to include trustworthy non-Muslim family in the process of marriage, seeking their advice and approval before embarking on such a tremendous life change (Al-Walaa Publications, 2008).

I was fortunate that Ahmad was a good man and that my family grew to accept him and even love him in their own way. However, not everyone is so lucky.

40

10

Self-Denial

◆

I had been married for several years when my depression symptoms returned. At the time, I had forgotten all about my initial visits to a psychiatrist and therapist in college. After I'd taken my *shahaadah* and abruptly quit therapy, I was on a spiritual high that all but erased my former life from my conscious mind. Looking back now with a bit more clarity and understanding of what was happening to me, I see how my convenient "forgetting" was merely my way of mentally disconnecting myself from the reality of who I was before Islam—and from the reality that she still existed.

In reflecting on what happened to me after I converted to Islam and thrust myself into the role of the "model Muslim," I am saddened because this experience gets to the heart of why understanding the human side of Islam is so important. But unfortunately, I had no idea what was happening to me and why. When my life fell apart so painfully and completely, I couldn't even turn to my religion for help because I genuinely thought that things like this didn't happen to practicing Muslims. Though living with a mental illness played a huge role in what ultimately happened to me, it hurts to know that so much of the collateral damage could have been avoided had I understood the human side of Islam.

In the Muslim community I was part of during this time, Islam was about continuous self-denial, and self-care was not even part of the equation. If I were to summarize in four words the underlying ideology of nearly everything I learned about my religion, it would be this: *The stricter, the better.* And more often than not: *The stricter, the only.* However, I don't mean to imply that I was completely ignorant of my faith and thus easily influenced by wrong concepts. Quite the contrary.

I had frequented Islamic classes so much after I became Muslim that I was ultimately hired full-time at the local Muslim school to teach Qur'an and Islamic studies. I also taught at the *hifdh* school on the weekend and enrolled in a *hifdh* program myself. Yet ironically, in all those years of studying my religion and teaching it to others, I never really learned or understood the essence of Islam. And here, I don't mean only the human side of Islam, I mean the *faith* side of Islam.

I knew the long list of *do*'s and *don't*s, and I adhered to every single one. But I genuinely had no idea that only some of those *do*'s were Islamic requirements while others were merely Islamic ideals. Also, I had no idea that some of the *don't*s were actual prohibitions while others were merely recommendations (or matters subject to permissible disagreement). Most tragically, I had no idea that I could do a definite *don't* and remain a Muslim at the same time.

When I was taught that Muslims don't drink, I took it literally. And why wouldn't I? No one had taught me I shouldn't. So for years, I genuinely imagined that if I ever took a sip of alcohol, I couldn't be Muslim anymore. And this terrified me. So I stopped drinking and went "cold turkey" overnight, literally.

However, the reality was that since high school, I had struggled with drinking. Initially, it was a social habit, but drinking eventually had become what I turned to in times of sadness. And battling undiagnosed bipolar disorder meant that my moments of "sadness" were many. By the time I reached college, I had a serious drinking problem, and I knew it.

I was never able to admit out loud my struggles with alcohol. Nevertheless, I really wanted to get the habit under control though I had no idea how. Any attempts I made toward sobriety were thwarted by my desperate and continuous need to escape the black hole of depression. Though I'd hate myself for it later, I'd find myself in front of the bottle over and over again. As the intoxicating liquid numbed my senses and quenched my ailing veins, I was able to drown out all my problems. But for the life of me, I could never fully comprehend what those problems were.

When I accepted Islam three years into college and was taught that Muslims don't drink, I stopped drinking. At the time, it really was that simple to me. So I never touched a drink again.

At least not then.

11

Hyper-Religiosity and Mania

♦

In the beginning, my bipolar symptoms resurfaced as debilitating melancholy. And I say "resurfaced" only because that is how I'd process it later. However, the truth is, my bipolar symptoms had never disappeared in the first place. When I'd recited the *shahaadah* and then stopped drinking and quit therapy, I was on a spiritual high that I know now was just the throes of mania. The super strict religious lifestyle I'd practiced and maintained for so long was just a result of hyper-religiosity, a classic sign of mania. But I fit in perfectly with the Muslim community I was part of, because hyper-religiosity was the exact type of Islam they practiced and required.

When I speak about the Muslim community's hyper-religiosity, I'm not suggesting that they were doing anything religiously wrong per se, or that they were in any way extremists. Rather I'm speaking of the collective mindset that does not allow for *others* to have varying points of view or to practice Islam differently from them. In their hyper-religiosity, they viewed all music as categorically forbidden and frowned upon television, movies, and even social media. So I myself left all of this alone, genuinely imagining this is what Allah required of me. At the time, I was completely unaware that this level of strictness was not the only legitimate way to practice authentic Islam.

So as to not be misunderstood, I'm not saying that this level of religious strictness is necessarily a bad thing. Though none of these strict practices are unequivocal religious requirements, there is definitely evidence in Islam to support this level of religiosity for those who desire it. Moreover, this level of strictness definitely works well for many people.

But it didn't work well for me.

Ultimately, I just could not sustain the level of religiosity that the community required. However, due to the manic side of my mental illness, in the beginning, I was able to maintain their required level of strictness with no problem. During that time, I fit in perfectly with the Muslim community because my hyper-religiosity mirrored their ideals of "the model Muslim."

Today I know that the community's mindset regarding the prerequisites to being a good, practicing Muslim was rooted more in ableism than Islam. Applying the rules and ideals of well people to the lives of the unwell simply does not work. In fact, it is quite harmful. Even for unequivocal religious requirements, like prayer and fasting, accommodations are made for the unwell.

If a person is sick and experiences difficulty in completing the required prayer movements, he or she may sit down for the entire *Salaah*. If a person has a medical condition that makes fasting harmful or unhealthy, he or she should feed the needy instead of fasting. And these are just two examples about how even basic requirements are adjusted to meet the needs of the unwell. How much more for things that are not basic requirements?

12

What Is Happening To Me?

◆

I was a wife and mother of two children when my hyper-religiosity began to break, and my depressive state began suffocating me. One of the first signs that there was a problem was that I just didn't have the energy to fulfill my duties as a wife and mother. I felt too exhausted to even get out of bed many days. Of course, in the beginning, I didn't know what was happening to me, so I pushed myself to get up and clean the house, prepare meals, and keep my husband company when he returned from work. But I felt like I was dragging myself through every task, none of which I was able to complete properly or fully. And I felt unmotivated to do any of them.

During this period, I was working full-time at the Muslim school, and I arrived late many days and was unable to prepare lesson plans. Additionally, my mother was diagnosed with breast cancer and was undergoing treatment, so she needed me to run errands for her, to help her around the house, and to drive her to and from appointments. She and my father had gotten divorced some years before, so after my sister, only I was available to help my mother. This added responsibility caused me to miss full days of work.

Whenever I was able to even partially fulfill something that was required or expected of me, a host of other responsibilities would remain unfulfilled. Because there were so many people depending on me, I neglected myself before I neglected anyone else. Though it wasn't a conscious decision, I stopped grooming myself and preparing food for myself. Eventually, I was unable to prepare meals for even my husband and children. I couldn't get out of bed. I was unable to comb my hair, and I was unable to take a bath.

It was during a community fundraising event that one of my friends pulled me aside and asked what was going on. I suppose by then my struggles were showing in my behavior and appearance.

"It's Ahmad's schedule," I told Tahirah. "I'm really stressed and overwhelmed because I hardly see him." As odd as it sounds to me today, that's what I honestly thought was at the root of everything that was happening. I thought the stress of taking care of the children, working full-time, and completing my daily tasks were becoming too much for me because Ahmad was often too busy to help me.

Ahmad did help out more, despite his long hours as a manager at work. He would come home and prepare dinner and make sure the children were taken care of. But he didn't have much success with me. No matter how much he talked to me, whether softly or firmly, I couldn't snap out of the neglect of myself or my family. But I wanted to. I really did. And I couldn't figure out why I couldn't.

13

Clarity After Confusion

◆

My undiagnosed bipolar depression continued to wreak havoc on my life until my husband and I agreed that I should see a therapist. This was 2006, nearly ten years after I'd seen a psychiatrist for the first time in college. We found a Muslim psychiatrist who was part of an Islamic community about thirty minutes from our home, and I made an appointment with him. It was after confirming this appointment that I recalled for the first time my initial visits to a mental health professional. Because I had forgotten all about it, I'd never mentioned to my husband that I had been previously diagnosed with depression and prescribed Prozac.

What propelled our final decision to make an appointment with a Muslim psychiatrist was my erratic behavior that was completely inexplicable to me. I hadn't been sleeping, and I was angry and agitated all the time. At times, I was yelling at my children at home or my students at school. At other times, I was euphorically happy and almost out of the realm of reality, beset with a flurry of ideas and hyperactivity.

One afternoon I mowed our home lawn six times with a push mower because I couldn't get it short enough. In my mind, it seemed to keep growing. When my neighbor expressed concern and asked me what was going on, I realized my irrational behavior and became embarrassed.

Initially, the Muslim psychiatrist, Dr. Saleem, diagnosed me with ADHD, attention deficit hyperactivity disorder. However, as I continued to see him and he came to understand the details of my various symptoms, he amended his initial diagnosis. He then explained to me that I had a classic diagnosis of bipolar 1 and was experiencing mania. He prescribed a mood stabilizer for me, and for the first time in years, I felt a sense of clarity regarding my struggles.

I immediately informed the administration at the Muslim school where I worked of my diagnosis. But I continued to work full-time, at least for the time being. However, I still struggled with preparing lesson plans and coming to work on time, and I still had to balance teaching with my home life and taking care of my sick mother. It wasn't easy. But the mood stabilizer helped tremendously in alleviating some of my depressive and manic episodes. However, it wasn't a cure-all. I was still living with bipolar and would have to learn to live with the reality of what that meant.

14

Rejected and Doubted

◆

I was eventually fired from my teaching position at the Muslim school. This hurt tremendously. But I understood why. No matter how angry and frustrated I felt, I couldn't deny everything I'd done that had led up to this moment. My frequent absences, my inability to complete lesson plans, and my outbursts in front of the children.

But I still felt blindsided.

Till today it hurts to remember the feeling of being unwanted. But I think I could have stomached it better had I felt the administration was inspired more by compassion than judgment when making the decision to let me go. I also think it would have been easier if they'd respected me enough to just let me know upfront of their decision. But they refused to even be honest with me. I was led to believe that I was still an employee even as they had already made the decision to not keep me.

At the time, I had been on leave due to struggles with my health and taking care of my mother, so there was a substitute who was teaching my classes in my absence. When things were better, I returned and approached the administration about setting up a meeting to sign my contract for the next term, and I was told a host of things to put me off. I was told to come back later. I was told that now wasn't a good time for the meeting. I was told that we could meet the following week. This went on for the entire summer.

Like most full-time teachers, I'd considered the meeting and contract signing a formality, so it didn't occur to me that I was in danger of being let go. It wasn't until that August when school was scheduled to begin that the administration finally told me that they would not be rehiring me and that the substitute teacher would be permanently taking my place. I felt like I'd been stabbed in the back.

Rationally, I knew they had the right (and cause) to let me go, so I didn't fault them for that. But I couldn't understand why they didn't let me know sooner. If I'd known at the beginning of the summer that I'd be without a job in the fall, I could have begun looking for work. With everything that was going on, I needed money and had already budgeted my finances based on my teaching income. Even with proper forewarning, I still would have felt hurt about being fired, but at least I could have had time to make other financial arrangements. However, more than the lack of professionalism, what hurts most when I think back to this time is combating the feeling that the Muslim community never really cared for me.

One of the first signs that I was not viewed compassionately came in a conversation with a Muslim woman whom I'd considered a friend and confidante. I was talking about my struggles with bipolar disorder, and she said flippantly, "They say bipolar; we say *Shaytaan.*"

In other words, she was saying that I was behaving irresponsibly because I was allowing myself to be influenced by the devil. It was her way of getting me to take responsibility for my actions. She felt I was using the mental health diagnosis as an excuse to misbehave without self-accountability. She was also saying that bipolar disorder didn't exist.

Hearing the callous dismissiveness in her voice made me question myself and my sanity. I wondered if I had indeed made it all up. *Maybe I am a bad Muslim*, I thought to myself. I thought of all the embarrassing things I'd done and wondered if somewhere deep inside, I'd done them all on purpose. I couldn't fathom why I'd *want* to humiliate myself and announce to the world my sins, but if bipolar disorder didn't really exist, I had no one but myself to blame for being unable to get my act together.

Another sign that I was not viewed compassionately was a community member implying that I was just an attention-seeking troublemaker. When I explained that I was struggling with mental illness and trying hard to balance everything that was weighing on me, they said, "Mental illness doesn't exist in my country," meaning that in their culture, people took responsibility for their problems.

Another community member told me that bipolar disorder and other mental illness diagnoses were just Western inventions that were contrived to deny the reality of sin and jinn.

I myself knew very well the reality of sin, jinn, and devils; and I didn't deny any of them. I also knew that, as the Prophet (peace be upon him) taught, all humans sinned; and I knew from both the Qur'an and prophetic teachings that the world of jinn and devils was an integral part of the reality on earth. Thus, I did not for a second imagine that having a mental illness meant that I was without sin or accountability in front of Allah. I also did not imagine that the world of jinn and devils never intersected with my life. However, being susceptible to sin and having some contact with the spirit world was a reality for every human being, but living with bipolar disorder was not.

But as I listened to one dismissive statement after the other and withstood Muslims saying that I was making all of this up, that bipolar disorder was not real, and that my "diagnosis" was just a Western invention, I began to wonder if they were right. Of course the psychiatrist who initially diagnosed me was a Muslim himself, so it made no sense to listen to the doubts of Muslims around me. Nevertheless, I did begin to question my sanity and wonder whether it was in fact un-Islamic for me to believe I had bipolar.

15

Drowning Alone

As I struggled to maintain my sanity amidst the repeated denials of my condition, I felt utterly incapable of stopping the avalanche of destruction crushing me. The more I listened to the Muslims in the community and imagined that I could fully control what was happening to me, the more out of control my life became. With every pitfall, I felt worse than before, so my paranoia and depressive states were repeatedly exacerbated. After several embarrassing manic and psychotic episodes in which I publicly humiliated myself, I asked my doctor for spiritual assistance in addition to medicine.

I had no idea what was happening to me and why I couldn't control the terrible things I was doing, so I felt the desperate need to be alone and heal without an audience. As the dismissive words of the Muslims repeatedly bombarded my mind, I realized the need to separate myself from the community if I were to have any semblance of sanity and hope for healing.

During my regular visits to the Muslim psychiatrist, I was reassured that bipolar disorder did in fact exist and that I was not imagining my symptoms or voluntarily behaving irresponsibly. However, I didn't feel that psychiatry was respected amongst the Muslims, so it was easy for me to doubt whether or not the psychiatrist himself was mistaken despite his expertise in medicine, mental health, and Islam.

In my frantic attempt to gain some semblance of dignity and self-respect as I tried to figure everything out, I asked Ahmad for a divorce. At the time, I imagined that even my husband did not understand what I was going through. Consequently, I didn't feel emotionally safe around him. I felt humiliated and embarrassed in his presence, as my mind kept hearing the dismissiveness and judgment of the Muslim community, and I projected it all on him.

Today, I know I judged Ahmad too harshly. Yes, it was definitely a challenge for him to wrap his mind around what was happening to me, and at times he himself couldn't quite accept the diagnosis. But looking back and knowing what I know now, I'm confident that it was a storm that he would have ultimately weathered by my side if I'd let him.

However, at the time, I felt like I was humiliating not only myself with my bipolar episodes, but Ahmad too. And I just couldn't live with that. It was difficult to work toward healing while imagining that I was a burden and an embarrassment to my husband. So just as I had years before when I decided to learn about Islam and practice the faith without anyone's help, I decided now to learn about my mental illness and heal without anyone's help.

16

Paranoia and Mental Breaks

◆

Though it seemed like the most sensible choice at the time, getting a divorce and separating myself from the Muslim community did not work out so well for me. I wanted to spend time alone so I could heal in peace, but that's just not how things panned out. Mental illness is not a condition that can be treated in solitude, and bipolar disorder is not a condition that can be fully "healed." However, I was still learning what bipolar disorder meant, and so much of what I believed about myself and my condition was influenced by the Muslim community I was part of at the time.

Although I had separated myself from them by not frequenting the masjid or community events, I couldn't separate myself from them entirely. Firstly, my children still attended the Muslim school where I once worked. Secondly (and most significantly), nearly everything I'd learned about myself and my faith had come from them. Thus, mentally and spiritually I was connected to them in ways I could not fully comprehend.

Many times when I was alone and lost in my thoughts, I remembered a lot of the embarrassing things I had done—not covering properly, getting tattoos, and having angry outbursts—and I'd shrink in humiliation and self-blame. I'd then spiral into a depressive episode realizing how the Muslims must think of me now. I imagined that it must be quite a pastime for them to spread my faults while discussing how "saintly Sakinah" fell from grace. I imagined all the horrible things they would be saying about me, and I would be overcome with both shame and rage. How could they be so mean to me? Why did they insist on backbiting me so relentlessly? What right did they have to mistreat me? Of course, I had no direct proof for any of these crimes, but I couldn't shake the feeling that I was the "talk of the town" in the community.

"I bet they're all talking about me," I told my friend Halimah one day.

"They're not talking about you, Sakinah," she reassured me. "You're just being paranoid." Halimah herself did not deny my mental illness diagnosis, but she tried to be my voice of reason whenever she felt I was losing touch with reality.

Halimah's denial of my fears stung, but I couldn't really argue with her. After all, I had no proof for anything I was saying. Yet still, I could not shake the feeling that I was being talked about behind my back—and not only privately, but publicly as well. Halimah kept telling me I was wrong. She herself was part of the community and had heard no talk of what I was saying. So she insisted that it was just my paranoia getting the best of me.

One day my imagination of being mistreated created in my mind an entire scenario involving a former friend who was still a teacher at the Muslim school. My mind recalled many things she had said and done, and I interpreted each of them offensively. With each offensive interpretation, I became indignant and infuriated. I could find no logical reason for her mistreatment of me except that she found something inherently wrong with me. I imagined she was like everyone else: judging me harshly because I was different. But with her, it wasn't because I was bipolar, my mind told me. It was because I was Black. *She's a racist*, I concluded at that moment, and then all of the mistreatment made sense.

Enraged, I sat in front of my computer and connected to the internet, determined to give my former friend a piece of my mind. I then typed a scathing email to her and listed all the horrible things she'd done and let her know I knew she was a racist. It wasn't until after I'd sent the email and my racing thoughts and paranoia calmed that I realized that none of it was true. I was then overcome with so much shame and guilt that I fell into a deep depression.

Ultimately, I realized that I was probably imagining the community backbiting me and publicly discussing my faults. Maybe Halimah was right. I was just being paranoid.

17

Confirmation and Fury

◆

Weeks later, I was having a relatively good day when Halimah called to apologize. It took me a moment to understand why she felt bad, but when I listened to her explanation, I became furious.

"I'm sorry, Sakinah," she said again after explaining the reason for her apology. "I shouldn't have accused you of being paranoid."

Halimah explained how she had gone to the school for an event and when she walked inside, a well-known member of the Muslim community was talking about me to another woman, saying terrible things. Even though Halimah and others were present, they made no effort to conceal my identity or hide my faults. Halimah ultimately spoke up and defended me, saying, "You know, Sakinah has an excuse." At that, one of the women was overcome with so much shame that she sat down and stared off into space as if the possibility had never occurred to her.

Halimah didn't tell me what was said exactly, and she didn't reveal to me who the women were. She had merely shared the story so that she could seek my forgiveness for accusing me of being out of touch with reality when I was in fact right. Halimah herself was so disturbed by the incident that I started comforting her. From her reaction, I knew that whoever was involved were not just average community members. These were people whom she, as well as other community members, had held in high regard.

Halimah was having a difficult time reconciling their good reputation and high standing with the public discussing of my faults. It was one thing to backbite someone privately while venting to a friend (which in itself was sinful), but it was another thing entirely to use a place designated for the remembrance of Allah to publicly malign a believer. They already knew I was diagnosed with bipolar disorder, so what was the point?

Days later I was still infuriated by what had happened. Not only was I enraged at the audacity of their unapologetic backbiting of me, but I was also enraged at what they had done to my friend. In some ways, I felt worse for Halimah than I did for myself. I was long past my "honeymoon period" of imagining I'd found a spiritual family and a "model Muslim community" after converting to Islam. From everything that had happened when I was fired and I was accused of using "bipolar" as an excuse to sin, I already knew that I was disposable and devalued by many members of the Muslim community. The hurt I had felt after I realized just how little I meant to them was excruciating, and I didn't wish that suffering on anyone. So it was difficult to witness that painful realization sinking in through the suffering of my close friend.

Like myself, Halimah had converted to Islam and had no Muslim family, so having a Muslim community to call her own was crucial to her spiritual well-being and emotional comfort. I hated that this fairytale had to be destroyed through her overhearing fellow Muslims talk so horribly about a friend she loved and cared for.

Though I felt some sense of vindication in realizing that I was not being paranoid in imagining that the Muslims were talking about me, this realization only exacerbated my real paranoia. How could I ever know reality from imagination if I was continuously surrounded by people who didn't care for me and who saw no problem with assassinating my character, both privately and publicly?

18

Public Deeds and Backbiting

Halimah wasn't the only friend who overhead me being talked about negatively in the Muslim community. There were others too, and each came and confirmed that I was not being paranoid and that they had defended me in my absence. However, one woman whom I considered a friend called to say that I deserved to be talked about openly.

"You're the one who's wrong," she said. "You made the choice to do those things publicly, so it's not backbiting if anyone talks about you."

As I held the receiver to my ear, I could hardly believe what I was hearing.

"In Islam," she explained, "it's only backbiting if we're talking about something you did privately. And anyway, you need to understand how difficult this is for the community."

"*What?*" I said, unable to keep quiet any longer. "Difficult for *them?*"

"Yes," she said, as if it were the most obvious thing. "It's really hard for them because they expected so much from you. They thought you were a good Muslim, and they can't understand why you're acting like this."

"So I'm supposed to feel sorry for *them?*" I said in disbelief.

"You at least need to understand that no one's wronging you. Public deeds aren't protected by the rules against backbiting. You know that." She spoke as if reprimanding me for even feeling hurt by the public spreading of my faults.

Hearing these cruel words was like being punched in the stomach. Here was a so-called friend confirming that I was indeed being talked about publicly, but then blaming me for *forcing* the backbiters to talk about me. According to her, I was the aggressor and the Muslim community was the victim. My mere imperfect existence was a crime against the standards they'd built for me. So I should take responsibility for the part I played in harming *them*.

They expected so much from you, Sakinah. Long after I hung up, I kept replaying her words in my mind, and with each replay, it was like being punched in the stomach over and over again.

There are public deeds, I read online some time ago. *Then there are deeds done in public. They are not the same in Islam.* In other words, the author was explaining that in our faith, everything that occurs in public is not considered a "public deed." Some things that occur in public are just deeds that happen to occur in public. In either case, both intent and circumstance are crucial to drawing a conclusion.

Actions are by intention is a famous prophetic hadith, and this principle applies very much to the case of a person suffering mania or psychosis, as I was during my so-called sinful "public deeds." However, even in cases of people not living with mental illness, everything done in public is not "fair game" for public discussion, and it certainly is not automatically removed from the category of backbiting.

For example, a Muslim might have a drinking problem and become weak and go to the store to purchase alcohol. Though the store is a public place, if another Muslim witnesses this purchasing of alcohol, this purchase is not necessarily a "public deed" that can then be spread to others without falling into the sin of backbiting. However, if a Muslim does a public speech, publishes an online video, or posts a blog stating that drinking alcohol is permissible, then other Muslims speaking up against this sinful "public deed" is not considered backbiting. In fact, the Muslim community would be obligated to clarify the true teachings of Islam regarding consuming alcohol.

But was it obligatory for them to talk about me? I wondered angrily. *Were there some blessings they believed Allah promised them if they spread my faults?*

Despite there being neither obligation nor blessings in the public spreading of my misdeeds, many Muslims in the community were so excited to have a religious excuse to backbite me. Because I had "chosen" to misbehave publicly, I allegedly no longer enjoyed even the basic rights of being their Muslim sister.

I wondered why this excuse to backbite was so readily embraced by them. It was as if they were waiting for an excuse to eat someone's flesh without falling into sin. And my flesh was what they enjoyed without the least bit of guilt or regret.

And I was supposed to believe *they* were the victim.

19

No Calls, No Visits

♦

I felt so abandoned and alone as I battled the ups and downs of bipolar disorder with almost no support. Halimah and her husband lived in a different city that was about an hour's drive from me, so I was left in the care of Muslims who had made it clear that they didn't value me except insomuch as I gave them an excuse to backbite.

What hurt most about learning of their consistent backbiting was realizing that they never really accepted me. I'd thought they loved and cared for me like a Muslim sister, and it cut deep to realize that they didn't even love and care for me like a fellow human being.

As I battled feelings of rejection and abandonment, I continued to visit my mother and help her around the house. Her cancer was now in remission, and she seemed to be doing much better. This was good news, but I myself was going through a difficult time. Dr. Saleem was the only Muslim who seemed to understand my struggles and would respond compassionately and appropriately each time. He never made me feel like a bad Muslim for having depressive and manic episodes, and he didn't try to convince me that *ruqyah* alone would solve all my problems. However, he did remind me that I should stay connected to Allah through prayer, *du'aa*, and reciting Qur'an to supplement my mental health treatments.

I listened to his advice and supplemented my medicine with *du'aa* and Qur'anic *ruqyah*, but I still battled debilitating depression. On more than one occasion, I was hospitalized in the psychiatric unit due to my suicidality and my fear that I would harm myself.

During my sickness, I spent day after day in the hospital, and I felt the depths of my loneliness. While other patients received calls and visits from loved ones, I received not a single phone call or visit from anyone. This was deeply hurtful mainly because I knew of the numerous prophetic narrations regarding the virtues of visiting the sick, and not a single Muslim showed up to get those blessings. Moreover, it was hard for me to reconcile their religiosity surrounding the alleged Islamic permission to backbite me, with their lack of religiosity surrounding the clear Islamic instructions to visit the sick.

When I was released from the hospital, I went home in a state of melancholy. I was no longer suicidal, but I was still lonely. I knew that no one would be there to greet me or welcome me or to say I was missed. My children lived with their father, but it was adult companionship that I longed. During this time, I wondered if I had even been mentally well when I made the decision to get a divorce.

As I battled my depressive and manic episodes, the mood stabilizer that Dr. Saleem had prescribed for me was helping tremendously. But I felt that it wasn't helping enough. Though I knew I wasn't supposed to, I began to increase my dosage of stimulants in hopes of feeling better faster and more often. Unfortunately, this ultimately led to me becoming addicted and suffering negative side effects. This addiction coupled with a sense of rejection and abandonment by the Muslims ultimately led me to drifting back to alcohol to comfort myself.

When I fell this far, I felt horrible and feared I was no longer Muslim. Everything I'd learned about Islam said that Muslims don't drink, so I thought I couldn't be Muslim anymore.

20

Sudden Compassion

◆

After being in remission for some time, my mother's cancer came back aggressively. The doctors didn't understand why this was happening, as she seemed to be doing fine previously. Facing this sudden bad news was extremely difficult for me, as my mother and I had grown so close. It was extremely difficult to see her so unwell. Though she herself had not become Muslim, she had always been supportive of me personally and spiritually. She had even become well-known in the Muslim community due to her frequent support of the school and Muslim events.

Somehow the news of my mother's deteriorating health and hospitalization spread, and many women in the Muslim community wanted to come visit her. Many of them were the same women who had abandoned me, spread my faults, and said I'd effectively concocted a mental illness diagnosis so I could do whatever I wanted guilt-free. They were the same ones who'd felt they were given permission in Islam to backbite me because my manic episodes were "public deeds." They were also the same women who hadn't called or visited when I myself was unwell.

To add insult to injury, I felt it was at least partially due to their abandonment that my depressive episodes were so severe and that my suicidality landed me in the psychiatric unit of the hospital—where these women didn't even feel it was necessary to call to check on me. But now, they wanted to visit my non-Muslim mother? Why?

"The sisters want to get blessings," Halimah explained to me on the phone. The apologetic tone in her voice told me that even she saw the contradiction and hypocrisy in this.

"*Blessings?*" I nearly screamed into the receiver, I was so irate. "Doing *what* exactly?"

"Visiting the sick," Halimah said tentatively, obligatory empathy in her tone. "Or maybe for *da'wah?*"

I grunted and rolled my eyes before responding sarcastically, "I think they taught my mother all she needed know about Islam with how they treated *me*."

Halimah did not push the subject, and I appreciated her for that. But I wondered if she expressed my hurt and offense to a few other women because days later some sisters gave me a call to explain why they hadn't called or visited in so long.

"We thought you weren't Muslim anymore," one woman explained, apology in her tone. She spoke as if she genuinely imagined that this would make it all better.

But you know *my mother isn't Muslim*, I responded angrily in my mind. But I was too upset to speak my thoughts aloud. After talking with Halimah, I had a fairly good idea where this sudden compassion was coming from. They wanted to show my dying mother how kind and caring Muslims were in hopes of her converting to Islam.

The hurt and betrayal cut so deep that I couldn't even think clearly after I hung up the phone. I was reminded of how kind and caring the community had been when I was the new Muslim, "Karen." I recalled how proud they were of me when I followed all the *do*'s and *don't*s they had outlined for me. I recalled how they put me on a pedestal and turned me into "the model Muslim" who was their spokesperson and promotional model at *da'wah* events. I recalled how good I felt about myself and my Muslim brothers and sisters at the time. I recalled how I'd actually imagined that I was part of a community, a faith family who would love and care for me no matter what.

We expected so much from you, Sakinah, I heard their condescending voices in my head. *How could you do this to us? Shame on you!*

Thinking of these women coming to my mother's bedside sent me into dysphoric mania, followed by psychosis, I was so triggered by what I felt was gaslighting.

21

Righteous Companions

◆

Fortunately, during this difficult time, I grew close to two Muslim women who would ultimately become my friends and lifesavers for years to come. Till today, I consider Malikah and Sabirah, as well as Halimah, my closest friends and the living examples of Muslims who understand the human side of Islam. Both Malikah and Sabirah were familiar with mental illness on a person level due to close family members struggling with similar issues to mine. Malikah was also studying psychology, and she hoped to pursue this passion by becoming an advocate for mental health.

What is ironic about our friendship is that much of the religious strictness that I myself was unable to maintain (and that the Muslim community insisted on), both Malikah and Sabirah lived seamlessly in their own lives. Both wore *niqaab* full time, and both viewed music as categorically *haraam*. However, unlike the hyper-religiosity taught in the Muslim community that abandoned me, neither Malikah nor Sabirah insisted that Islam could only be practiced in a way that mirrored their personal choices. Both were very aware of the dangers of ableism and thus did not expect everyone to be carbon copies of themselves. They also understood the nuances of both *fiqh* and mental health and thus differentiated between foundational and clear matters, and issues that allow some level of flexibility in practice and understanding.

Like all friendships, we have our disagreements, but in their presence I've never felt judged or shamed for being a Muslim woman living with the realities of mental illness. This is in sharp contrast to how I still feel about myself amongst most women in the Muslim community I was part of for so many years.

Till today I view having Malikah and Sabirah in my life as a mercy from Allah. Both have saved my life on more than one occasion, and both have offered me their homes when I had nowhere else to go. And neither of them ever abandoned me when I needed them, and they never shamed or blamed me for being human.

22

Losing Mommy

◆

As my mother's conditioned worsened, I spent hours with her in the hospital each day, and we laughed and talked together. We even managed to have some debates, like old times. She would tease me about my stubbornness, and I'd tease her about hers.

One of my fondest memories during this time was when my friend Tahirah came to visit my mother in the hospital. "I want to invite you to Islam," Tahirah said to her over the phone. To my pleasant surprise, my mother smiled wide and said, "I've never been *invited* before." She was so moved by Tahirah's invitation to Islam that she couldn't stop talking about it. Listening to my mother go on and on about how honored she was by Tahirah's invitation, you'd think that my mother and I never had a single conversation about Islam in all our years together. But I'd never used the expression, "I *invite* you to Islam." So I suppose that's what made the difference.

In any case, I was just happy to see my mother so happy, and it made all the difference that her being formally invited to Islam was lifting her spirits. Tahirah continued to talk to my mother about Islam, even when my mother could no longer speak in response. And my mother never refused the conversation, and she seemed so pleased with Tahirah's invitation.

When my mom died, I experienced a break with reality. I was in a daze for several days, and then weeks afterward. One thing that sticks out in my mind is the imam of the Muslim community texting me to express his condolences. This really touched my heart and showed me that the women who had been mistreating me did not represent the heart of the community. When my mother was alive, this imam was her favorite speaker, as she was constantly moved by his humility and good character.

In his text, the imam asked if I needed anything and if I had eaten that day. I told him that I hadn't. It took a while for him to convince me to allow him to bring me some food, but I eventually agreed.

That night, I remember him walking quickly up the hill leading to my front door carrying a large bag. "You need to eat, Sakinah," he said as he handed me the bag. The sweet aroma from the warm bag comforted me and made me realize that I indeed needed to eat.

I stood for a moment and watched as he hurried back down the lawn and drove away. Today, my memory is spotty due to the combination of my mental illness and medication, but I remember standing there in the doorway that night holding a bag of warm biryani and *naan*. For the first time in a long time, I felt that I was cared for in the Muslim community, that I was not forgotten, and that I was no less valuable because I was bipolar.

In a word, as I closed the door and settled down to eat the warm meal, I felt loved.

PART III
Mental Health Advocacy

"One of the things that baffles me (and there are quite a few) is how there can be so much lingering stigma with regards to mental illness, specifically bipolar disorder. In my opinion, living with manic depression takes a tremendous amount of balls... At times, being bipolar can be an all-consuming challenge, requiring a lot of stamina and even more courage, so if you're living with this illness and functioning at all, it's something to be proud of, not ashamed of.
They should issue medals along with the steady stream of medication."
—Carrie Fisher, *Wishful Drinking*

23

Becoming 'The Muslim Hippie'

◆

With all the things I've been questioned about and criticized for as I struggled with bipolar disorder (before and after the diagnosis), I shouldn't be surprised that there is some confusion and judgment surrounding my nickname "The Muslim Hippie." This is the name I've chosen for my online mental health advocacy work because I feel it suits me. But apparently, to some Muslims I cannot be both a Muslim and a hippie. I suppose it's similar to the mindset of those who believed that I could not be Muslim and have a diagnosis of bipolar disorder. But living with bipolar is a condition that I did not choose, whereas being a hippie is a description I chose for myself because it resonated with who I've always been as a person.

I spent the early part of my youth in Hyattsville and Takoma Park, Maryland, and there was a large hippie population there. Of course, at the time, I was not Muslim, but because I was a "free spirit" I considered myself a hippie. When I got really sick, I was admitted to a hospital in Takoma Park, and it was there that I got my life back.

When I first chose the online name "The Muslim Hippie," I didn't think much of it. I was just creating a new name for my Twitter account, and the name @TheMuslimHippie resonated with me. At the time, I had no idea that my social media persona would become relatively familiar in the mental health community, and I had no idea that the nickname would take on a life of its own. However, the name grew on me, and I eventually started blogging as "Sakinah, the Muslim Hippie." I think the first time I realized the popularity of my chosen handle was when I traveled for a conference and some of the participants saw me and said, "Oh, you're 'The Muslim Hippie' right?"

Generally, hippies are known for their lack of conformity to societal norms, their advocacy for peace and love, their simple lifestyle and connection to nature, and their unique artistic expression. I would say all of these characteristics applied to me during my youth, and they still apply to me today. Living with bipolar and being Muslim means that I do not conform to many societal norms by default. Being both a Muslim and a spokesperson for mental health means that I advocate for a social and political climate that fosters peace, love, and compassion for disabled people of all faiths. Both my spirituality and my mental health advocacy encourage simplicity and good health, which often can be gained through interacting with nature and eating healthful foods. Personally, I've always been inclined toward creative expression, whether through writing or art. In these ways, I am still a hippie today. And because both my faith and personality are integral parts of who I am, I am truly "The Muslim Hippie."

Naturally, I don't have all the characteristics of everyone who considers themselves a hippie. Like any group, hippies are not a monolithic group. I don't know what being a hippie means to others who use the title, just as I don't know what "free spirit" means to everyone who uses the description. I can only speak for myself. And to me, being a Muslim hippie simply means I am a free spirited woman of faith who advocates for people to be respected as full human beings in society.

24

Understanding Bipolar Disorder

◆

"We thought you were just having fun," a friend of mine told me once as we were discussing my life with bipolar disorder. Hearing this confession hurt, and it just added to the numerous wounds I'd sustained in the Muslim community. I certainly don't think of my manic episodes as "fun" no matter how elated and wired I felt during each one—or how happy I *looked*.

Perhaps the best way for neurotypicals to understand bipolar disorder is literally: *bi* meaning two states, and *polar* meaning the extremes of these polar opposites. Bipolar was formerly called *manic depression*. This initial name was in reference to these two states: mania and depression. But mania is not happiness, and depression is not sadness. There is more to bipolar than mania and depression. Both states are so much more than that, and so much worse than that. Both mania and depression are destructive, and neither can be fully controlled, at least not in my case.

Mania is like jumping off a cliff while imagining you're flying, and depression is like drowning while having no arms or legs to save you and no voice to scream for help. You cannot "rationalize" yourself out of manic episodes, and you cannot "think" yourself out of depressive states. What makes mania *manic* is that your rationale and judgment are severely impaired, and what makes depression *depressive* is that you cannot pull yourself out of it, no matter how much you want to.

Advice like "think before you act" or "just think positive" doesn't work for people living with bipolar disorder. During both states, you feel as though there is no tomorrow. You simply do not and cannot think beyond the here and now. This is what makes bipolar a disorder and why many are in fact disabled due to living with the disorder. In mania, you don't consider or realize the consequences of your actions because tomorrow does not exist in that state. In depression, you don't comprehend or realize the possibility of a better day because the debilitating here and now is all that exists.

Though mania is not insanity medically speaking, it is not far from it figuratively, and though depression is not paralysis physically speaking, it is not too different from it mentally.

However, this does not mean people living with bipolar disorder have absolutely no control over their actions and decisions. It just means that their judgment and array of choices are severely impaired, and what works in the mind of a neurotypical may not work in the mind of a person with bipolar. Therefore, all internal and external behavior management must meet the bipolar person where he or she is at that moment—not where we want them to be.

Since manic and depressive states are rooted in immediacy (i.e. what is happening right now), all responses to the episodes must also be rooted in immediacy, whether this response is by the person herself or by someone wishing to help. For example, when I am manic, I have difficulty controlling my impulses, and since my rationale is impaired, I cannot simply list all the reasons why I should not do such and such and then stop myself from doing it. Thus, I remain in the present and focus on realizing I'm manic and working from there. I do this by either taking my medication, calling someone who can help, or going to an environment where I know I cannot act out like I am inclined to. I do the same with depression except I cannot go to another environment since I am effectively paralyzed into inactivity. Sometimes I (or my friends) have to take me to the hospital.

25

Starting Mental Health Advocacy

◆

I didn't set out to become a mental health advocate. I was just struggling with my disorder and trying to make sense of my life. I needed to vent, and I consistently went to Twitter to do it. With all that I'd withstood from my brothers and sisters in Islam, I was feeling suffocated in shame, and I refused to remain silent any longer. Social media gave me an outlet.

For a person living with bipolar disorder, social media is both a blessing and a curse. On the one hand, you have the freedom to speak your mind without anyone censoring you or silencing you. But on the other hand, that same freedom makes you susceptible to posting some pretty humiliating and scathing stuff. In my anger and need to vent, I had several meltdowns on Twitter. Some were so embarrassing that I just deleted the entire account afterward. But I'd eventually open a new account and start again under a new name.

In the beginning, I think it's safe to say I was just using my various handles for Twitter rants. I'm not sure I'd consider that stage of my social media presence "mental health advocacy" per se, but in its own way, it was the beginning of my online work. Ironically, I think what was most significant in these rants ultimately laying the foundation for my advocacy work was the mockery and cruelty of others in response to my continuous meltdowns and restarting various accounts. Some people who knew me through this erratic behavior would make fun of me and send me offensive messages about what I'd said or done during a manic or depressive episode.

One tweet I remember vividly was a woman saying to me "Girl, get your life together!" When I read this, I felt horrible about myself. And I thought, *If I could, I would.* I really wanted to get my life together, but bipolar disorder made that goal continuously elusive for me, at least in a way that others could appreciate. Also, people would send me DM's asking, "Are you okay?" or "What's going on with you?" But it was not with compassion. It was with derision.

Some people would claim to be therapists and then proceed to say condescending things to me under the guise of giving me advice. I have no idea if some of them were truly therapists in real life, but they came across as severely judgmental, not empathic or caring. I don't know how, but some of them got ahold of my phone number and called me saying, "You know, you really need to pull yourself together." Then they would lecture me while claiming to be mental health professionals. But there was no real therapy going on. It was a one-sided conversation with them talking down to me, and it was very mean-spirited and callous.

In the face of this online and offline bullying, I would often post explanations of what had occurred in hopes of people understanding that I hadn't been in my right mind during those posts. If it was a phone call, I'd say to the person, "You know, I'm not well. I'm having an episode." Sometimes my explanations were clear and concise, other times they were jumbled and emotional. Sometimes I would respond angrily, other times, I would respond calmly. Fortunately, some of the people were receptive, but others were unflinching in their claims that I was just making excuses so I could do whatever I wanted.

At this time, I had no intention to be a spokesperson for bipolar disorder. I was just trying to protect my dignity, reputation, and character. I imagined that if others could understand my challenges, they wouldn't see my episodes as humorous, sinful, or signs of bad character.

During this time, my friend Malikah started an online mental health support group, and she asked me to join and help out. I agreed. This support group was relatively private and aimed at offering support to Muslims who either struggled with mental illness themselves or who had loved ones struggling with mental illness. We supplemented this initiative with a blog, and contributing to this blog was my first official job online blogging as a mental health advocate. But even then, I didn't consider my work especially significant. We didn't have many readers or followers, so I just thought of my writing as talking to a small group of supportive friends.

When I selected the Twitter handle @TheMuslimHippie, I told myself that I wasn't going to delete this one, no matter how embarrassing my tweets were during an episode. It was my way of accepting myself and not apologizing to anyone for being how God created me. One thing that emboldened my unapologetic stance was coming across a book on Amazon entitled *Forensic Psychiatry in Islamic Jurisprudence* by Kutaiba S. Chaleby.

As I read Chaleby's book, I felt both vindicated and enraged. Here was a board certified Muslim psychiatrist saying in print everything that the Muslim community said had no basis in Islam. And to top it off, much of his experience and references came from research based in both

Islamic sciences *and* the country Saudi Arabia. Meanwhile I had been told that my mental illness didn't exist in Islam or "Muslim countries."

Interestingly, Saudi Arabia was the one country that this particular Muslim community effectively idolized. Many of them had lived or studied there, or wanted to. Yet I was made out to be an "unstable" person for dealing with some of the exact symptoms listed in a book based in research from psychiatry work in that country.

I could have screamed, I was so relieved and infuriated at once. I kept thinking to myself, *They called me crazy, and I found this information on Amazon! Amazon, of all places!*

Yes, I already had a Muslim psychiatrist who had validated my illness, but finding this book on such a well-known site just solidified for me everything Dr. Saleem had been trying to tell me all along. But the feelings of betrayal that I felt as I read the book left me without words. I couldn't believe I'd been accused of concocting a mental illness so I could violate the rules of Islam. Meanwhile, my mental illness itself was discussed under the rules of Islam!

So no, I was not going to be quiet, and I was not going to let anyone off the hook when they tried to shame me for being both bipolar and Muslim.

26

The 'Real' Sakinah

◆

"Sakinah knows exactly what she's doing," one Muslim woman who considered herself my friend said in response to my initial explanations about what was going on with me. In her mind, I was misbehaving "on purpose" and needed to be corrected firmly. "She wasn't like this in college," other Muslims said, implying that I had created an entirely new persona under the guise of suffering from bipolar disorder. They had been with me in the MSA (Muslim Student Association) in college after I'd become Muslim; thus, they had effectively assigned themselves as authorities on "the real Sakinah."

Not only were these statements deeply hurtful and invalidating, they were completely untrue. Though I had been experiencing mania during the incidents that my "friend" was referring to, I hadn't even met any of the college MSA members until I was twenty-one years old. So how would they know who I "really" was? We had spent less than a year together during the time period over which they claimed authoritative knowledge of my "real" self. I'd had a whole other life before they met me, and they had been privy to none of it.

What I find most ironic about the claims that I had "suddenly" changed was that I'd met these women only *after* I'd recited the *shahaadah*, the testimony of faith marking my official entry into Islam. Given their cultural practices, their strict interpretations of Islam, and their assuming the role as my spiritual teachers, there was no real opportunity for us to get to know each other in any significant way. The relationship we'd had was primarily one sided: They were my instructors, and I was their student. The only part of myself I shared with them was the part that they'd specifically asked me to: how I'd learned about Islam and become Muslim.

In Islam we are taught that all our previous sins are wiped away at the recitation of the *shahaadah* and that we effectively enter the faith as faultless as newborn babies. We are also taught to cover our faults and to not speak unnecessarily about our sins. So I'm unsure what these women are referring to when they speak about who I "really" was back then.

They didn't know me, and my newfound faith (at least as I'd understood it at the time) required me to remain silent about that time period.

Because the Muslims had been so moved by my *shahaadah* story, they'd continuously asked me to share it on *da'wah* forums and at Muslim open house events. As I mentioned earlier, I'd fulfilled this role willingly and proudly. However, I never for a moment imagined that this decision was an implicit statement that I had been a saint before I was Muslim. It honestly never occurred to me that I was implying anything at all by agreeing to share my story and become an active member of the community. My love of Islam was sincere, as was my love of my new faith family. In my naiveté, I'd genuinely imagined that this was all that mattered in being embraced as their Muslim sister and becoming a valued member of the community.

Unfortunately, when some Muslims hear of stories like mine with bipolar and that of other American Muslims with their spiritual struggles, they attribute our problems to our ethnicity or our "newness" to Islam. Derogatory terms like "convertitis" are used to describe our initial spiritual zeal and our later "laxity" or "mental breakdowns." Recently, someone I'd met at the Muslim school posted on my social media page stating that mental problems like mine are common among converts to Islam. She said that our problem was that we put unnecessary burdens on ourselves by wanting to practice Islam so strictly, but then we have mental breakdowns later.

Reading those words was like being stabbed in the heart. Here was a woman who felt no empathy or compassion for someone she'd met and interacted with in the Muslim community. She felt no connection to me as a fellow Muslim. She didn't even feel respect toward me as a fellow human. Because I was neither of these to her. Had I been the same person but from her cultural background, I wouldn't have received the same treatment. To her, I was just a pathetic, broken American convert suffering from self-inflicted wounds due to the burdens I'd put on myself.

Even if we forget momentarily that mental illnesses like bipolar disorder are not unique to Americans, the fact that she divorced her culture and people entirely from my negative experiences, as well as from those of other American converts, speaks volumes. Why didn't it occur to her that a large part of our "mental breakdowns" is due to the religious teachings and treatment toward us by people of her own background? After all, who is teaching so many of us Islam after we convert? Who is placing these "unnecessary religious burdens" on us in the first place? And whose mistreatment of us is sending so many of us into breakdowns—or away from Islam entirely?

This woman's words hurt me deeply, I cannot deny. But they did not surprise me. She was only voicing aloud what is often said about American Muslims in private. In predominately Desi and Arab Muslim communities, American converts often are not fully embraced as members of the community, and this situation is exponentially worse for Black converts. The behavior codes of respect and working together that are signatures of these cultures amongst themselves are denied to "outsiders", even if they are Muslims.

In these predominately immigrant Muslim communities, American converts are often used as promotional models to show the American public the "beauty of Islam." However, they don't have much value for us beyond that. In hopes of eradicating Islamophobia—and of securing for themselves a comfortable American life—we are invited to speak at their "About Islam" events as the "safe faces" of Islam to the general public. Then when these communities have no further use for us, we are cast aside to fend for ourselves. We are not part of their cultures and families, so we are not a part of their lives in any meaningful way. The idea of a "faith family" is promoted only insomuch as we Americans help *their* causes, even if it is at the expense of ourselves.

When we are no longer able to withstand their continuous disregard for us as full human beings and we speak up or "break down", they frown at us in contemptuous pity and withdraw from us completely. "Look what happens when these Americans try to practice Islam so strictly," they say, obligatory sympathy in their tones. In this, they completely ignore the central role they themselves played in our "religious instability" and "mental breakdowns."

For many American converts, these experiences feel very much like being victims of abusers who wonder aloud what's wrong with their victims who have emotional and mental struggles following the trauma. Then the abusers use the victims' struggles as proof that the victims were the problem all along. It is like experiencing the saying: *You take out my eyes then scoff at me for being blind.*

Personally, I can attest to the difficulty of battling both bipolar disorder and the mistreatment suffered by American converts in general. So many of my mental struggles were attributed to some inherent character flaw in me or to my decision to "suddenly change" so that I could leave off Islamic principles and enjoy myself. Even if I had suddenly changed overnight, this in itself is a hallmark sign of mental illness—not bad character.

In no way do I suggest that I have no accountability to my Creator for any of my errant behavior during bipolar episodes. I know I have to meet Allah on the Day of Judgment like everyone else, and I do not know what I will be excused for and what I must answer for. And naturally, the reality of this Day terrifies me. However, ultimate Judgment of my behavior, intentions, and accountability are for my Lord alone to decide, not anyone else.

27

A Social Worker Gave Me Back My Dignity

◆

I felt so horrible about myself by the time I was admitted into a hospital program for people living with mental illness. The social worker heading the program was a tough, no-nonsense woman who made it clear that she did not feel sorry for us. She was there to help us get our lives together, but she would not be pampering us along the way. The truth is, she made me nervous and uncomfortable. In some ways, she even scared me.

One thing that solidified for me that she was not going to let us get away with anything was when one patient, with similar diagnoses as mine, was unable to comply with some basic rules of our program and was subsequently dismissed as a result. We had been asked to follow certain procedures in order to begin to gain control over our diagnoses and lives, and to show that we weren't letting our situations dictate our behavior (when possible).

The first time that I learned that she even saw anything good in me was when she was reprimanding the group one day and helping us see our past missteps and the need to correct them, and she said, "You all should be more like Karen." She then started listing my praiseworthy attributes for them to bear in mind.

It took a moment for me to even realize she was talking about me, as it had been so long since I'd heard anything positive said about me. I had begun to assume I was a bad person with bad character because that's how the Muslim community made me feel. They simply had been unable (or unwilling) to see beyond my bipolar episodes and appreciate the sincere struggling person underneath. However, here was a social worker doing just that.

The social worker gained nothing personally through speaking about the good she saw in me. From our interactions during the hospital program, I can't even say that she liked me very much. Of course, if she had, she probably wouldn't have shown it in any obvious manner. But despite having full knowledge of my "sins" and errant behavior during my manic and depressive episodes, she was able to discern Karen the person from the bipolar episodes that often afflicted me.

What made this discernment significant to me was that everyone in the program struggled with mental illness, and the social worker faulted none of them for it. However, she had a keen eye for recognizing underlying good character and self-accountability despite the external manifestations of mental illness. Not only did she see both in me, she also concluded that, in her view, I was foremost in exemplifying the best of both, so much so that she continuously used me as an example for other participants to look to in weathering their own trials.

I left that program with an entirely fresh and improved view of myself, not only as a person but also as a Muslim. The irony of this source of inspiration did not escape me, as the woman did not even share my faith. It would take several years before the Muslims in my community became more respectful of me and receptive to my explanations regarding my challenges. But I continued to take heart in the blessing that Allah had sent me in allowing a non-Muslim social worker to give me back my dignity.

28

Legally Disabled

◆

I didn't become Muslim to be abused. This is what my heart said over and over as I fought the rage I felt at the mistreatment I experienced from the Muslim community during my bipolar episodes.

"You can't blame them," some friends have said in defense of the Muslims who abandoned me and spoke negatively about me during my illness. "They're not doctors, so you can't fault them for not knowing what was going on with you."

I've thought on this point myself many times, but it offers me little solace and relief. I understand ignorance. I really do. I myself was ignorant of my illness for many years. But I honestly don't believe ignorance is what inspired their mistreatment of me. Ignorance inspires a complete loss at what to do, not a deliberate decision of mistreatment. Ignorance might even incite some innocent carelessness, but it never incites cruelty.

Stigma. That's what was underlying much of their mistreatment of me. Because I was suffering from behavior that allegedly took away my right to be treated kindly, they felt completely free to talk negatively about me and treat me harshly. It didn't hurt that I was also an American convert (i.e. not one of them), so that made me doubly stigmatized.

Sakinah knows exactly what she's doing. This is what I'd hear over and over in my mind as I struggled with manic and depressive episodes. Knowing the non-Muslim social worker's positive conclusion about me helped tremendously, but unfortunately, it was not enough to silence the self-doubts incited by the Muslim community's negative assessment of me.

When I stood before a judge who was to determine whether or not I was eligible for disability due to my mental health struggles, I began to explain to her some incidents that had occurred during my bipolar episodes. I started to tell her of some of my errant behavior and the things said about me in the community. I'd imagined that it was only fair that she heard all the perspectives concerning me. At the time, I was unsure whether or not the community had been correct in stating that I knew what I was doing.

However, the judge wanted to hear none of it. She was interested only in my medical records, my hospital stays, and what my doctors had said about me. Though today it seems a rather obvious approach, at the time, I was surprised that the judge wasn't interested in the circumstantial accounts of those who had delivered their assessment on me for years.

It was at that moment when I was declared legally disabled by the judge that I think I began to really understand the significance of the gifts Allah had given me through Dr. Saleem, my closest friends, and the compassionate social worker—and even through the book I'd found on Amazon. This understanding gave me a determination to remove the stigma surrounding mental illness in the Muslim community, and I would use this clarity and inspiration to inform my mental health advocacy work.

PART IV
Living With Bipolar Disorder

"Creativity is closely associated with bipolar disorder. This condition is unique. Many famous historical figures and artists have had this. Yet they have led a full life and contributed so much to the society and world at large. See, you have a gift. People with bipolar disorder are very very sensitive. Much more than ordinary people. They are able to experience emotions in a very deep and intense way. It gives them a very different perspective of the world. It is not that they lose touch with reality. But the feelings of extreme intensity are manifested in creative things. They pour their emotions into either writing or whatever field they have chosen."
—Preeti Shenoy, *Life Is What You Make It: A Story of Love, Hope and How Determination Can Overcome Even Destiny*

29

Moving On

◆

When I speak about my mental health advocacy work today, I think of it as two-faceted: what I do in "real life", and what I do online. I consider "real life" advocacy when I participate in mental health conferences, when I talk to people in person, or when I participate in live events or forums about mental illness. I consider online advocacy when I blog for different websites and when I use my social media handles to spread awareness about living with bipolar disorder.

Months after I became Muslim, I sat on a panel to share my *shahaadah* story to curious non-Muslims. At that time, I never would have imagined that I would be, years later, published in major media outlets sharing my story about living with bipolar disorder. Moreover, I would have never imagined that many of the women I'd considered friends and part of my faith family wouldn't be there by my side to support me.

I'm no longer angry with them for not supporting me. But I cannot deny that the memories of everything that happened still hurt me at times. Today I have a cordial relationship with the Muslim community. However, I'm not friends with many of them, and I don't imagine I ever will be. I still have Malikah, Sabirah, and Halimah whom I visit and speak to regularly; and these women are tremendous blessings and more than enough for me. So I am eternally grateful to Allah for placing them in my life.

Fortunately, the Muslim community in my area has stepped up and been helpful to me whenever I needed *zakaah*, so that's a marked improvement over their treatment of me in the past. I also recently spoke to one of the administrators at the Muslim school about me doing workshops to help the teachers and other staff understand mental illness better. As awareness about bipolar and other mental illnesses has become more popular in the media, the Muslim community has begun to see my diagnosis as something that can affect anyone. Consequently, they no longer treat me as harshly as they once did.

Some community members have even opened up to me and shared that they have family members facing similar struggles, and that some of the students at the school have mental health issues as well. Nothing has been officially set as of yet, but the opportunity of my being a voice of awareness in my former Muslim community looks promising.

Nevertheless, not all of the old wounds have been fully healed. When I visit the masjid on occasion, there are still signs that I am not entirely welcomed. I recently experienced a woman not returning the salaams. I also experienced a woman crossing to the other side of the hallway at the sight of me and reciting Qur'an to protect herself from my presence. This offended me, but not as much as it would have years ago. I no longer define myself by their thoughts and treatment of me, so I can more easily view behavior like this for what it is: their problem, not mine.

I've let go of the anger and bitterness and have forgiven the ones who wronged me, at least insomuch as their wrongs relate to our dealings in this world. And I've asked Allah to heal me from fear of judgment and shame from those still learning to accept my illness. My *du'aa* is that I don't cause undue harm to another person because of what I'm going through. And I ask Allah to reward me for the times I experience difficulties from others as well. Thinking of this divine justice has given me the strength and tranquility to move on, and I find that sharing what it is like to live with bipolar disorder helps tremendously in maintaining this strength and tranquility.

30

Anxiety, Multiple Stigmatization, and Marriage

◆

Anxiety is one of those beasts that is very difficult to tame. Once it surfaces, it can spiral into a zillion difference experiences including panic, paranoia, and even psychosis, depending on where my brain takes me at a given time. Anxiety can be incited by real or imagined events or just by my general knowledge of how things normally go or what I've experienced in the past.

One topic that consistently incites anxiety is my desire to get married. Here is where I'm stigmatized multiple times over. I am Black American. I am a Muslim woman. I am a convert. I am divorced. I am the mother of three children. I live with bipolar. Why does this multiple stigma incite anxiety? Because in each layer of stigma, I am robbed of a bit of my human existence, and my right to *be* human.

Even without bipolar disorder, this multiple stigma is difficult to overcome. But when you throw bipolar into the equation, the stigma is exacerbated tenfold. As awareness of bipolar and other mental illnesses are becoming more talked about in the media, I am finding that the public reception to hearing about the struggles of the illness is improving greatly. However, this acceptance is still one-dimensional: I am only allowed to exist as a voice of bipolar disorder, not as a voice of the human being beneath that disorder.

Thus, the public acceptance of the intersectionality of bipolar disorder and natural human intimacy is largely missing. To a lesser degree, a similar lack of acceptance exists for divorced women in America. However, for the divorced Muslim woman in America, there isn't only a lack of acceptance, there is also a deliberate pushback against both her desire to remarry and her right to choose any partner God has made lawful to her.

In many Muslim communities, there is still a link between piety and asexuality, especially amongst Muslim women, and this link is even more pronounced amongst divorced Muslim women. Muslim women are expected to have no sexual desires, and divorced Muslim women are expected to be content being single for the rest of their lives. In only very rare cases is the divorced Muslim woman allowed to have a voice of her own, as others continuously speak on her behalf. For this reason, divorced Muslim women have come to be looked at as soul-less charity cases to be taken care of by any Muslim community (or man) who wants "the blessings."

Moreover, even when Muslim leaders give lip service to divorced women *not* being charity cases, these leaders go on to speak on our behalf and define for us what this should mean. In doing so, they remove from us our full humanity by denying us the basic right to human choice. Sometimes their solutions make the concept of being a "charity case" more appealing to me.

When Muslim men discuss divorced women, especially in the context of disparaging the option of plural marriage, I often want to shoot back, "How dare you speak for me!" But I say nothing because I already know I won't be heard. With a single social media post or lecture at a Muslim event, I am silenced, dismissed, and denied my existence all at once. There really is nothing I could say on this topic without incriminating myself further. I already "need" to get married, and because I am a divorced mother of three, this need has somehow become a trait of shame in the Muslim community.

Besides, even if were to speak up, I would be disrupting the Muslim status quo, which wishes to paint the picture of "good Muslim men" as being strictly monogamous. This lauded station of modern day piety equates abandoning divorced women and single mothers with honoring them. When I hear over and over again "good Muslim men" distancing themselves from this permissible option, I feel as if they are saying that their elusive Muslim image matters more than the actual Muslim women. It is also as if they're saying to the West: "Look at us! We're not focused on sex! Look at all the single and divorced women we abandon every day, and we have no intention whatsoever of marrying any of them!"

"Be patient," I'm constantly told whenever I bring up the difficulty of living alone as a divorced woman with no husband to care for me. *You deserve more than the options that Allah has given you*, I keep hearing the translation of what they're really saying to me. But then they walk away with their husbands and wives while imagining I should be patient in my loneliness.

What I find interesting is that the advice of being patient moves in only one direction—mine. Why don't *you* be patient? I wonder. Especially when it comes to my struggles and needs. Why can't part of this necessary patience be about stepping up to take care of women who are unmarried? Why is patience always about us suffering in silence and waiting for a phantom single man to show up?

31

Depression, Isolation, and Suicidality

◆

During my lowest points, I read the verse in the Qur'an that says, "Men are the maintainers and protectors of women," and I thought begrudgingly, *For me, they're not.* But I'm in a much better place now, and Allah has shown me that there are men in the *ummah* who take their role as *qawwaam* seriously. Even Ahmad is helpful to me whenever I am unwell though we are no longer married. And he also supports me financially when needed. This has given me solace during some of my more difficult moments.

But it still hurts to see posts where Muslim imams, public figures, and Islamic teachers make statements that appear to be looking out for the honor and well-being of single, widowed, and divorced women, but in fact only contribute to the wider culture of harm, dismissiveness, and abandonment of them. Far too many posts and speeches are given about us and ostensibly *to* us, but very little to no real work is being done to actually honor and support us practically. But somehow we're supposed to believe this manmade code of honor when it comes to marriage: *You deserve more than the options that Allah has given you.*

And I think to myself, *Really? What could that be, and who's offering it?*

When I vent to my friends about my frustrations, they continuously remind me to be patient, and this just frustrates me further. Often they're sitting on the phone snuggled comfortably under the arm of their husband, telling me to be patient with a lifestyle they themselves would never choose. I know they mean well, and I know they don't agree with the widespread abandonment and disregard for divorced women that is rampant in the Muslim community in America. But their words just remind me of how insignificant I really am in the eyes of other Muslims.

Sometimes when I hear a lecture mentioning the mercy of Islam and how Muslims care for all of creation, even plants and animals, I have to resist the urge to groan and roll my eyes. I have come to understand these statements for what they are in most Muslim communities in America: theoretically true on paper, but practically almost non-existent for most

Muslims. In my view, there is far more "marketing" of Islam to non-Muslims than there is actually *living* Islam amongst Muslims.

I couldn't even get the treatment of a dog, I've thought angrily at times whenever I heard the famous prophetic hadith about Allah forgiving a prostitute who gave water to a thirsty dog. My anger was inspired by my memories of having first been fully embraced by the community as a promotional model for the Muslim brand, and then being ultimately abandoned and cast aside during my time of need.

We thought you left Islam, I keep hearing the Muslims say in defense of themselves. But these same Muslims still manage to show up to raise hundreds of thousands of dollars in crowd-funding campaigns for non-Muslims if they think it will help the "image of Islam" in America. But I couldn't even get help in having running water in my house. This is difficult to swallow.

The painful memory that I speak of is when I was living alone, penniless, and couldn't even afford to have my water turned back on. I couldn't take a bath, make *wudhoo'*, wash my clothes, or even flush the toilet. I lived like this for some time without anyone knowing because the Muslims didn't bother to check on me when they imagined that my "sinful" manic episodes meant I'd left Islam. Apparently, getting tattoos, slitting my wrists, not covering properly, and drinking alcohol removed all my rights as a Muslim woman. You'd think witnessing a fellow Muslim battling these struggles would inspire Muslims to help me *more*, but that's precisely when they abandoned me. Then they used the evidence of my need for their help as their divine excuse for refusing it.

Fortunately, when Malikah discovered what was happening, she immediately stepped in and offered me her own home, where I stayed for quite some time. But I'll never forget how the isolation from the community just exacerbated my depression during that time.

If you want to understand what I mean by "depression", know this: Depression is *not* sadness. It is a monster that sits on you and doesn't let you breathe. You can't think positive thoughts or say "nice things" to make the monster move. It's a monster, so it doesn't even know that language. And you can't push the monster off of you because depression is like paralysis that is rooted in the mind instead of the limbs. So it's like being suffocated by a monster while you have no use of your arms or legs.

To understand the mental experience of depression, picture this: Imagine going into a long, narrow paper bag headfirst, and you can't get out. The only path your mind processes is the one in front of you, so you don't even think there's a way out. You're not thinking clearly, so you're actually confounded. You don't see light at the end of the tunnel. In fact, there is no tunnel. It's just a mass of darkness blinding you and suffocating you at once.

In this darkness, it's just bleak. There is no tomorrow. It is what it is, period. Here's where the suicidality kicks in, and to add insult to injury, suicidality is its own illness. In this state, you're not in your right mind. So again, thinking "happy thoughts" just doesn't cut it. Let's not forget that the monster is still sitting on you when you become suicidal.

Understand this and understand it well: A mentally ill person who is homicidal to themselves does not even process hope, let alone think of it and apply it logically to themselves. For a person living with bipolar disorder and experiencing suicidality, there *is* no hope, period. It simply does not exist. And no, I'm not talking about a person consciously disobeying Allah and wanting to take their life due to avoidable despair. I'm talking about mental illness here. The former is a fantasy that a person concocts to escape life's troubles, and the other is a mental reality in which a person cannot stop themselves. They're entirely different experiences.

Personally, I've had to call Malikah on many occasions to help me when I feared I could not stop myself from ending my life. Fortunately, she responding to my call every time and never once berated me for being a "bad Muslim" for having these thoughts. She came and helped me or took me to a hospital where I could get help, every time.

"There is no sadness in Islam," Muslims often claim when discussing depression. By far, this is one of the most hurtful forms of erasure that I've ever heard.

This proclamation doesn't even exist in theory, so I'm unsure where Muslims got this idea. In the Qur'an, there is the story of Prophet Jacob (Ya'qoob), the father of Prophet Joseph (Yusuf), going blind when he was without his beloved son for many years. There is also the story of Prophet Muhammad falling into such deep sadness after his wife Khadijah died and revelation stopped for some time that Allah revealed an entire soorah of Qur'an to comfort him.

So many Muslims have yet to accept that practicing Islam is not mutually exclusive to being human.

32

Health Struggles and Worship

◆

One of the most difficult times of year for me is Ramadan. I often have nostalgia recalling my early days as a new convert to Islam. At that time, I was able to fast the entire month and break fast with the community. I had moments of difficulty in fasting back then, but before I was properly diagnosed, my hyper-religiosity and mania shielded me from the reality of my illness.

In a blog published via patheos.com, I reflect on my recent struggles during the Muslim holy month:

> This year it has been a major challenge for me to stay connected with activities that will enhance my faith and keep me close to my community. For some reason I've been having a lot of trouble keeping my bipolar and anxiety symptoms under control. This has dramatically impacted how I'm observing the month.
>
> It can be demoralizing to feel mentally unwell during such a blessed and peaceful time. You often wonder what you're doing incorrectly that's preventing you from using your spirituality to help you weather hardships. This alone can result in harmful negative thinking and self-loathing; which directly affects your faith. A major struggle has been not letting self-deprecating thoughts about my situation discourage me from doing the best I can religiously, especially when I feel like giving up.
>
> Once someone asked me if I could use specific prayers and verses from the Qur'an to help me begin to heal mentally and emotionally. On

paper I understand why this seems like a simple solution. But what I explained is that when your judgment and thinking are clouded by mental instability, you often lack the clarity needed with which to allow your belief system to help you (June 11, 2017).

"Be like a bee." This is one of the most profound pieces of advice an imam gave me in balancing my mental health struggles with my worship as a Muslim. At the time, I had come to him desperate for any *du'aa*, prayer, or verse from the Qur'an I could recite to help me through my more difficult bipolar episodes. I was even willing to enroll in any Islamic class that would help me heal.

In response, instead of listing specific prayers I could say, the imam reminded me to be patient with myself and my illness, and to take only what I could handle from Islamic teachings about spiritual healing. He told me that I should continue to read the Qur'an, make *du'aa*, and recite specific prayers for help through my difficulty, but that I should not overwhelm myself by fixating on anything specific as a cure-all for my episodes. In applying anything I learned, I should take whatever benefited me given my circumstance then move on to nourish myself with something else. This is what he meant by his advice to "be like a bee." It was like I was moving from "flower" to "flower" for that bit of nourishment I needed for my own purposes.

"But if you want a specific *du'aa* that can help you," he said, "then recite the prayer of Yunus." In this, he was referring to the prayer that the Qur'an narrates that Prophet Jonah (Yunus) said when he was trapped in the whale and wanted Allah to deliver him from this fate: *None has the right to be worshipped except You [O Allah!], and glory be to You. Indeed, I have been amongst the wrongdoers.*

This suggestion resonated with me on so many levels, as it was a reminder that I was not living in the world of normal people. I was like a person trapped in a dark place and circumstance that others could not fathom or understand. In facing this, it was only Allah who could help me through this. And Allah did not ask me to carry the burden of anyone but myself. Thus, I should not fall into ableism in applying the spiritual norms of well people to myself, especially when I was battling the manic and depressive episodes of bipolar disorder.

33

Shame, Religion, and Mental Illness

◆

"What is going on with you?" a Muslim friend of mine asked me during one of my manic episodes. "You know better!" When I explained to her that I couldn't fully control what was happening to me, she said, "You know exactly what you're doing." And then she added, like others had before her: "They say psychosis, and we say *Shaytaan*."

Till today, these words still sting. At the time, my friend imagined that she was being firm with me as she "forced me" to get myself together. When I think on this overly simplistic (and harsh) advice often given to people living with bipolar disorder, I wonder why mental illnesses are not treated as real while physical illnesses are. Yet both are realities in medicine and religion.

"There's no blood test for mental illness!" a woman said to me, as if this was proof that bipolar disorder did not exist.

I had to hold my tongue from saying something flippant in response. There is no blood test for a host of things, including the existence of *Shaytaan* and jinn. But how would she, as well as other mental-illness-denying Muslims, feel if someone used this scientific argument to deny the existence of the spirit world or even God Himself? Even if she and other Muslims argued that jinn and God existed because Islam said so, then why deny mental illness when Islam also verified its existence too?

I have no idea why so many Muslims are insistent upon denying the reality of mental illness diagnoses and continuously refer to them as "Western." Yet these same Muslims fully accept a host of medical diagnoses from Western medicine, many of which are not mentioned anywhere in Islam. Naturally, the Qur'an and prophetic narrations are not meant to act as a PDR (physician's desk reference) for mental and medical illnesses, so it is completely irrelevant whether or not a specific mental or medical diagnosis is listed in them. However, given that both medical and mental illnesses are confirmed as realities in the Qur'an and prophetic narrations, it is ironic that many Muslims accept only the specifics of the former and then put everything else in the broad category of *Shaytaan* or jinn.

No, a mental illness diagnosis is not mutually exclusive to someone being bothered by *Shaytaan* or jinn. But the same is true for a medical illness diagnosis. In Islam, the suffering of the Prophet Ayyub (Job) due to being afflicted physical illness is well-known. Yet many Muslims ignore the implications of his words about this illness as quoted in the Qur'an: "And remember Our slave Ayyub (Job) when he invoked his Lord [saying], 'Verily, *Shaytaan* has touched me with distress (by losing my health) and torment (by losing my wealth)" (*Saad*, 38:41).

Moreover, even if someone is tested with an illness (medical or mental) rooted in the work of *Shaytaan*, how does this justify disregarding them or denying the specific label given to it in the West? I've never heard Muslims disregard cancer or heart disease as "Western." Why then do they disregard bipolar and other mental illnesses as Western—as if a "Western" diagnosis is somehow incompatible with Islamic reality?

The shame that I and other Muslims experience as a result of this repeated denial of our reality is indescribable. However, it is a blessing that this arrogant ignorance is not characteristic of all Muslims. In every Muslim community, I'm sure there are people like Dr. Saleem and my friends Malikah, Sabirah, and Halimah. They may be the exception. But that doesn't make them any less real. With their compassion, understanding, and support, I have been able to get both spiritual and medical assistance for my bipolar disorder, including proper medication that has greatly reduced the extremities of my episodes and allowed me to live a relatively healthy bipolar life.

34

Music Therapy

◆

I don't know if there's a topic more controversial than music amongst Muslims, and unfortunately, I wasn't protected from this often bitter disagreement. As is the experience of so many sincere American Muslim converts, my first lessons about music were strict and unequivocal. The community that I was part of after I converted to Islam told me that music was categorically forbidden in Islam and that to listen to it was similar to drinking alcohol and engaging in forbidden sexual behavior. Consequently, I stayed away from it completely and didn't ask any questions. Like so many other things that I abandoned in the name of religion during that time, it didn't occur to me that I wasn't being told the full truth about music.

It wasn't until after I experienced my friends' dismissal and abandonment of me during my manic episodes that I began to question their strict definition of Islam. I knew something was wrong when I experienced so much love and acceptance from them when I was their "model Muslim" at work and *da'wah* events but then was dropped like a hot coal when I needed them to be "model Muslims" for me. All the prophetic stories I'd heard from them about the kindness, compassion, and support in Islam evaporated into a cloud of legend. When I needed that kindness, compassion, and support from the very Muslims who'd shared the prophetic stories with me, these "legends" became relevant only at "the time of the Prophet."

This was my first hint that the Islam I was being taught did not match the Islam that reflected the life and teachings of Prophet Muhammad, peace be upon him. As I began to regain some semblance of the unique identity I'd had as the independent, carefree "hippie" Karen before I'd accepted Islam, I started to explore other Muslim communities' understanding of concepts like music. I was surprised to learn that other legitimate points of view existed on the topic of music, and it hurt to learn that not a single one did my Muslim community acknowledge as even valid.

Because it opened up the opportunity to learn more about my faith, my being abandoned by my original Muslim community turned out to be a huge blessing for me. Perhaps, if it hadn't been for their harsh treatment of me, I would have never learned about the more lenient views on music and the validity of music therapy itself as a supplemental treatment for bipolar disorder and mental illness in general.

It was both freeing and empowering to read from other respected Muslim scholars evidences that music was allowed in more than the strict voice-only interpretation of my original Muslim community. Learning this opened up the door to me to explore what was available to me in music therapy as a bipolar Muslim. From this research, I learned of illnesses being treated and cured with music therapy and with even elderly people in nursing homes coming out of depression with music therapy. Today, I use music therapy myself at times, and it helps tremendously with my anxiety and depressive episodes.

35

Suicidality and Islam

♦

The following is an excerpt from Sakinah's blog at
patheos.com/blogs/themuslimhippie:

My first bout with suicidal feelings was in high school. I remember sitting in the dark basement one night and wishing I could suddenly disappear forever. I was afraid to take my own life though, because my dad had always taught me that a person of faith didn't have the right to place themselves in the Creator's position and choose life or death. Yet I desperately wanted to die. My soul was in complete agony. I couldn't see a way out of my painful existence and I didn't know where to turn for help. I couldn't imagine this suffocating feeling would ever end. It was intolerable. I curled up in a ball and silently prayed for peace and for God to let me go. I hoped it wouldn't hurt.

Since becoming a Muslim, suicide has been a sensitive subject. I've always known that my religion unequivocally forbids this action. But the tricky part is, at what point does my mental state come into play in a case like this? If I were manic and emotionally dysregulated, and then made the decision to attempt suicide, would Allah hold me accountable if I completed the act? Or would he forgive me due to my inability to think clearly. Would my impulsivity come into play? What if I were unable to stop myself due to being in a state of psychosis? What if my bipolar depression caused me to dissociate and I couldn't appreciate the full impact of my actions? I wondered all these things and more during a period of mental instability. As my health declined, I became increasingly delusional, disillusioned with my life and the world. I spent a cold winter night in 2015 deciding whether or not to end my life, as I've done so many times before. On this occasion, loneliness and paranoia had overtaken my mind, and I felt as though the universe was out to get me. What other explanation was there for my misery? I felt like I couldn't exist anymore and that I deserved Allah's punishment for being a bad person. I hated myself and I imagined everybody else did as well. I didn't want my kids to have a mother like me. I felt happy that their stepmother was someone I respected and could trust to take care of them in my absence. Nobody needed me here anymore, my time was up. That's what I thought anyway.

Eventually I got through that night safely. And I recovered from my suicidal feelings. But I was left with a sense of confusion about suicide in Islam. I didn't feel this was a subject I knew enough about. One thing I kept dwelling on was the idea of causing myself harm whether intentionally or otherwise, and how it's handled in the American psychiatric community. Whenever I've been a danger to myself, I've received inpatient psychiatric treatment until I was mentally healthy. Twice it was made clear that this treatment was mandatory for my safety and that it was apparent I wasn't able to make life-affirming choices. When I did a cursory exploration into the basics of Islamic law concerning mental health and competency, I found that the treatment for someone like me was quite similar. I have the right to hospitalization and psychiatric treatment not only for my safety, but for my general wellbeing. And if it becomes clear that I'm unable to make that choice for myself, involuntary hospitalization may become a necessary step. Upon reading this, I realized I had more questions about the *fiqh* of mental health in Islam and about suicide. If measures were in place to prevent me from harming myself, could it be that suicide/suicidality for someone living with mental illness may be a complicated issue requiring in depth study?

Another question that arose around this time was that of self-harm. I couldn't reconcile how, though I've always known suicide is forbidden, at times I've knowingly been on the brink of making this fatal choice anyway. This means that some part of me may have known Allah might be upset with my choice and I might have been willing to place myself in a position to be ultimately judged for my major mistake. That a person would knowingly harm themselves is one of the reasons hospitals, doctors and sometimes even law enforcement steps in to stop them. The person's judgment is temporarily impaired, and it's then up to others to get them to a place of safety and security until they're feeling better. So even the very notion of suicide appears to be one that fits into the larger category of self-harm. It's its own illness that requires specific treatment and care. I vowed to research this topic further and begin asking necessary questions of those who had studied Islamic law. It's not that I was planning to commit this deed. Just that the fear of not knowing about a part of my life and something that affects people in my mental health community caused me to want to understand it from an Islamic perspective. Stigma surrounding mental health and suicide in Muslim communities made me fearful to ask about this topic. But I knew I didn't have a choice if I wanted to know the full truth.

Suicidality and Mental Illness

In *Forensic Psychiatry in Islamic Jurisprudence*, author Kutaiba S. Chaleby says:

> Suicide is a condemned act in most of the known religions in the world. Christianity, Hinduism, and Buddhism all condemn suicide. Islam carries that further and declares that people who commit suicide will be condemned to hell. With this stand against a person taking his own life, Islamic scholars have maintained the position that suicide is an unforgivable sin.
>
> [In the cased of attempted suicide] Islam has maintained a strong position against assuming other people's intentions... According to Islam, in a suicide attempt by a mentally disturbed person, he or she will be covered by the rule of insanity in which Islam holds strongly that an insane person is not responsible for his acts. If we consider the principle of the *Safeeh*...where a person recklessly and irresponsibly acts against his own best interests, Islam has given the state the right to make decisions for this person. We can by analogy (*Qias*) propose that a suicide attempter is acting against his own personal interests and should be protected from himself through a voluntary or involuntary hospitalization (p. 121).

36

Closure and Self-Acceptance

◆

The following is an excerpt from Sakinah's blog at
patheos.com/blogs/themuslimhippie:

The hospital is the great equalizer.
I always say I happened into writing about mental health because of my own story, and then my advocacy ideas came about later. I often gloss over the first part, because to me it's the least interesting chapter of how I got to where I am in my life. But I realized something recently when I was processing some feedback from one of my readers. By not telling the story fully, I've missed details that explain why I'm so passionate about my style of advocacy.

I've mentioned on many occasions that I've been hospitalized in the inpatient unit 7-8 times over the years. That's at least 28 days in the hospital with other mental health patients, many of them Muslim, and from all different countries. For statisticians, no, I wouldn't have an exact number, unfortunately.

Two patients that stand out to me are a disabled sister and a father of four. I'm unable to give any more details because of privacy laws. But the sister's interaction with me was really touching. When she saw me approach the intake desk, she was standing with another patient. She shouted and walked over to hug me. I didn't understand what the commotion was about. It turns out she didn't know we could be covered [in hijab] inside the unit. In years past, women had to remove their scarves for safety reasons. I had a flashback to my first inpatient stay when a polite but naive nurse asked me if I wanted to wear hospital grade underwear in place of my scarf. That was the only material she could find and she didn't know what else to do. At the time, there was no one else like me to relate to in my area. I felt lost emotionally, spiritually and physically. It was one of the worst nights of my life.

At this hospital, upon seeing me in my scrubs and scarf the sister was completely overcome. She was emotional both at seeing another Muslim and at the fact that we could cover. I understood her elation and teared up with her. She went to the nurse's station and requested her hijab. At least we could have some semblance of dignity while we were there. I've been wearing my hijab since 1996. It's become like a second skin, so I don't even think about it sometimes. But both nights, the one where I was in a public hospital with strangers and had nothing to cover my head, and the one where a sister I didn't know hugged me too tight because she could cover hers, were the most influential nights of my life with the hijab. I've never thought of it like that until just now.

Her story isn't unique. I've met many sisters like her over the years. And brothers who've had to take time away from work and their families to address their mental health needs as well. The joy and relief seen on the face of a fellow Muslim is touching and heartbreaking. You're happy to meet a brother/sister, yet crestfallen that they know this life test. The stories are full of hope, sadness, and everything in between.

I hope not to have to go back to the hospital anytime soon. It would mean my symptoms have come back and need emergency management. But if they do, I hope to see a friendly face on the inside so I don't have to be alone. That's always the best part. Allah has been truly merciful.

FINAL NOTES
Managing Mental Illness and Helping Communities

37

A Difficult Journey

◆

Treating my diagnosis has been a difficult personal journey. I've learned a lot over the years, and I've also made many mistakes. For the strictly clinical part of my illness, I've been blessed to be able to rely on the experience I gained working as a certified nursing assistant. Patient care helped me learn how to take the human side of illness into consideration and listen to what people need. It's also helped me learn how to advocate for myself and explain my symptoms clearly, even when in crisis.

I've written articles in the past about living well with bipolar and how to be your best self. In truth, however, I'm always unsure how helpful my advice has been to other patients and for those trying to learn about mental illness.

Firstly, what works for one person may or may not work for another. Secondly, some people are disabled by their mental illness while others are still able to live a full life with their diagnosis. Meaning, those realities are separate and should be handled differently. Finally, different communities and cultures may take different approaches to mental health and mental illness.

I don't want to speak for all bipolar patients or for all Muslims with mental health issues. As such, I'd like to conclude my story with a few self-care steps I take to make my days brighter; rather than giving general advice for living with mental illness. In addition to medication, I have a standard regimen that helps me remain grounded, even when I'm episodic. Following this chapter is a starter mental health diary where individuals can begin to write their own ideas of what self-care means to them. The diary (and prompts) can be continued in one's own journal.

38

Personal Tips and Mental Health Diary

◆

Here are some spiritual supplications and recitations that I use daily as a form of meditation to calm my mind and to invoke Allah's help:

1. *Du'aa* of Prophet Yunus (Jonah), which he recited while trapped inside the whale: *Laa ilaaha illaa anta. Subhaanaka. Innee kuntu min adh-Dhaalimeen.* None has the right to be worshipped except You [O Allah!] Highly glorified are You! Verily, I have been amongst the wrongdoers.

2. *Du'aa* recited after each of the five obligatory prayers: *Allaahumma antas-Salaamu wa minkas-salaam tabaarakta yaa dhal jalaali wal ikraam.* O Allah! You are the Source of Peace, and from You comes peace. Blessed are You, O Owner of Majesty and Honor.

3. *Du'aa* recited by one whose circumstances have become difficult: *Allaahumma laa sahla illa maa ja'altahu sahlan, wa anta taj'alul hazna idhaa she'ta sahlan.* O Allah! There is no ease except in that which You have made easy, and you make the difficult, if you wish, easy.

4. Last three chapters of Qur'an, which have been translated to mean the following:

Soorah 112, *Al-Ikhlaas* (The Sincerity or Purity of Faith): Say, "He is Allah, the One and Only. Allah, the Self-Sufficient, Eternal. He begets not, nor was He begotten. And there is none co-equal or comparable unto Him."

Soorah 113, *Al-Falaq* (The Day Break): Say, "I seek refuge with the Lord of the day break, from the evil of created things, from the evil of darkness as it overspreads, from the evil of the witchcrafts when they blow on knots, and from the evil of the envious one when he envies."

Soorah 114, *An-Naas* (Mankind): Say, "I seek refuge with the Lord of mankind, the King of mankind, the God of mankind, from the evil of the whisperer who withdraws [after his whisper] who whispers into the breasts of mankind, amongst jinn and men."

Aromatherapy: I use an oil diffuser in my room regularly to soothe my generalized anxiety disorder, and to assist me during manic episodes. When I'm in a depressive state, filling the room with various scents helps elevate my mood, even if temporarily. Aromatherapy is also very useful when I'm dealing with the effects of noise sensitivity. It helps calm my nerves and allows me to sleep until my moods are more regulated.

Journaling: I use a journal to write my thoughts during all of my mood episodes. Describing how I'm feeling and giving a voice to my thoughts helps channel my emotions. It can relax a racing mind and direct errant ideas. If I'm experiencing bipolar anger, writing in my journal helps me get out my frustrations and let them rest on a page instead of directing that energy outward. Journaling can also help me fill the emotional void when I'm depressed. Allowing my hurt to flow through my pen lessens the pain I feel from my moods.

Advice for Caregivers, Friends, and Communities: Check on your loved ones and regularly ask if people are doing all right. Regular check-ins can help people who aren't able to reach out in times of distress.

When someone exhibits signs of mental health problems or a specific mental illness, do your best to assist them in seeking professional help and let them know you care. It can be frightening and confusing to suddenly not understand your brain and symptoms. The sooner one gets the right help, the sooner they are more likely to get back on track and have the ability to manage their issues.

Never try to fix or handle mental health challenges by yourself. Mental illness is a complicated set of disorders that requires professional intervention.

The best way to combat stigma in Muslim communities is with proper education and by talking. Ignorance and fear thrive in silence. Though Muslims try to handle life challenges with patience and grace, mental illness requires one to talk regularly and describe any issues. Communities should have open conversations about mental health, and individuals should be encouraged to talk about their challenges, in order to address symptoms. The only way a professional can understand how the mind is functioning is for a person to describe what they experience.

There are trained experts in the mental health field, even in the Muslim world, both here in the United States and globally. Just as Muslims follow the leadership and tutelage of those who have studied Islam and have certain credentials, we must treat scholarship in psychiatry with the same reverence and respect. Doctors, psychiatrists, peer counselors, emergency psych staff, Islamic leaders with mental health training, etc. are those we should defer to for guidance, help, understanding and education. Individual patients the world over have the right to choose how they handle their own health. However, when it comes to speaking publicly about mental health or helping people seek assistance, we should allow those with proper knowledge do the talking. It saves lives.

Self-Care Journal with Prompts

Use these starter questions to begin a diary entry. Use your own diary to continue this exercise on subsequent days.

What is your mood today? (Do an online search of sample mood words if you need guidance)

_____

_____

_____

_____

Name one goal you'd like to accomplish by the end of the day. (Nothing is too small or big; this is for you!)

_____

_____

_____

_____

On a scale of 1-10, how would you rate your motivation level? (1 being lowest, 10 being highest) _____

Name one thing you can do today that will make you feel good about yourself.

_____

_____

_____

_____

Name one thing you will do today for your personal hygiene (includes living space)

_____

_____

_____

_____

What does self-care mean to you?

_____

_____

_____

_____

On your best day, how would you imagine your self-care regimen to be?

_____

_____

_____

_____

On days when you are unable to engage in self-care, how do you support your mental health?

_____

_____

_____

_____

Follow Sakinah, 'The Muslim Hippie'
Twitter: @TheMuslimHippie
Instagram: @The.MuslimHippie
Blog: patheos.com/blogs/themuslimhippie

Follow Umm Zakiyyah
website: uzauthor.com
Facebook: facebook.com/ummzakiyyahpage
Instagram: @uzauthor
Twitter: @uzauthor
YouTube: youtube.com/uzreflections

Also By Umm Zakiyyah
If I Should Speak
A Voice
Footsteps
Realities of Submission
Hearts We Lost
The Friendship Promise
Muslim Girl
His Other Wife
UZ Short Story Collection
The Test Paper (a children's book)
Pain. From the Journal of Umm Zakiyyah
Broken yet Faithful. From the Journal of Umm Zakiyyah
Faith. From the Journal of Umm Zakiyyah
Let's Talk About Sex and Muslim Love
Reverencing the Wombs That Broke You: A Daughter of Rape and Abuse Inspires Healing and Healthy Family
And Then I Gave Up: Essays About Faith and Spiritual Crisis in Islam
I Almost Left Islam: How I Reclaimed My Faith
The Abuse of Forgiveness: Manipulation and Harm in the Name of Emotional Healing
even if.

Order information available at uzauthor.com/bookstore

About the Author

Umm Zakiyyah is the bestselling author of the *If I Should Speak* trilogy, *Muslim Girl*, *His Other Wife*, and the self-help books *The Abuse of Forgiveness* and *Reverencing the Wombs That Broke You*, written for religious survivors of family abuse. Her novel *His Other Wife* is now a short film.

She writes about the interfaith struggles of Muslims and Christians and the intercultural, spiritual, and moral struggles of Muslims in America. Her work has earned praise from writers, professors, and filmmakers and has been translated into multiple languages.

To learn more about the author, visit uzauthor.com

REFERENCES

Bekiempis, V. (2014, February 28). Nearly 1 In 5 Americans Suffers From Mental Illness Each Year. *Newsweek.com.* Retrieved May 2, 2017 from http://www.newsweek.com/nearly-1-5-americans-suffer-mental-illness-each-year-230608

Chaleby, K.S. (2001). *Forensic Psychiatry in Islamic Jurisprudence.* Herndon, VA: International Institute of Islamic Thought.

Kaiser, K. (2017, June 11). Ramadan: Addressing My Mental Health & Processing Shame. *Patheos.com.* http://www.patheos.com/blogs/themuslimhippie/2017/06/11/mental-health-challenges-ramadan-dealing-internal-shame/

Kaiser, K. (2017, July 20). Souls Matter in Mental Health. *Patheos.com.* http://www.patheos.com/blogs/themuslimhippie/2017/07/20/souls-matter-mental-health

Kaiser, K. (2017, December 10). Suicidality As a Muslim Part 2. *Patheos.com.* http://www.patheos.com/blogs/themuslimhippie/2017/12/10/suicidality-muslim-part-2/

Umm Zakiyyah (2011) *Realities of Submission.* Camp Springs, MD: Al-Walaa Publications.

Made in the USA
Lexington, KY
17 March 2018